# THE GENERAL THEORY OF
# ELECTRICAL MACHINES

## This Book

is one of a series recommended for publication by the
Technical Papers Panels of
ASSOCIATED ELECTRICAL INDUSTRIES LTD.

# THE GENERAL THEORY OF ELECTRICAL MACHINES

*by*

## BERNARD ADKINS
M.A., D.Sc., M.I.E.E.

**THIRD PRINTING**

LONDON

## CHAPMAN & HALL LTD.

37 ESSEX STREET W.C.2

1962

*First Published 1957*

*Reprinted, 1959*

*Reprinted, 1962*

© BERNARD ADKINS 1957

*Catalogue No. 548/4*

REPRINTED BY LITHOGRAPHY AND BOUND IN GREAT BRITAIN BY
JARROLD AND SONS LIMITED, NORWICH

# FOREWORD TO THE A.E.I. SERIES

*by* THE VISCOUNT CHANDOS, P.C., D.S.O.,
*Chairman of Associated Electrical Industries Ltd.*

THE books in this series have been produced for those concerned with advanced theory and practice of engineering and kindred subjects. There is a growing need for such books, particularly overseas and in the countries of the Commonwealth.

Great Britain has both the special knowledge and the experience that gives birth to new technologies and supports them while they are growing. It is not enough to have such knowledge if we hide it under a bushel, and it must be widely disseminated. Much of it is found in the industrial organizations, and it is their duty to spread it through the medium of articles and books. The staffs of all such organizations should be encouraged to publish their work for the benefit of all.

It is with this purpose that the A.E.I. Series of textbooks has been founded. It is an extension of an earlier series sponsored by the British Thomson-Houston Company—one of the A.E.I. Group—and its aim is, by including contributions from all the member companies of A.E.I., to make knowledge of a wider range of subjects available to engineers and technologists.

*Chandos*

# PREFACE

The electrical machine is still, in spite of all recent developments, the most important and fundamental type of electrical apparatus. All but a small fraction of the electrical power in use at the present time is produced in a generator, and more than half of this power is used to supply some type of electric motor. The study of electrical machines is an essential part of any course in electrical engineering. Moreover, in spite of the fact that this subject has been studied for a longer period than most other electrical topics, there is plenty of scope for further developments both in practice and in theory. The theory of electrical machines is not a static subject, and it has now reached a point where the rather piecemeal methods of the past need to be co-ordinated in order to provide a more powerful line of attack on new problems. This book presents a general treatment of electrical machine theory, which gives greater uniformity between different branches of the subject and points more clearly the way for future investigations.

The book is based on a course of lectures given in 1951 to graduate students at Imperial College, London, and to a group of design engineers at Rugby. It is a result of work carried out over a period of twenty years while I was employed as a designer and consulting engineer with the British Thomson-Houston Company, Rugby. Much of the material is derived from American papers, which, however, are rather scattered and in need of co-ordination. The sources are acknowledged where possible in the bibliography. In particular the basic idea of a generalised electrical machine was first put forward by Gabriel Kron, who developed the theory in terms of matrices and tensors. The present book requires no previous knowledge of these rather advanced subjects, although some of the simpler methods of matrix algebra are introduced in the last chapter. It does not deal at all with the application of tensors to machines, although it is hoped that it may serve as an introduction to Kron's work.

The book is intended for students and others who already

have some knowledge of electrical machines, as it does not include any description of their construction. The mathematics required include differentiation and integration, and complex algebra. The Heaviside operational calculus is used for several problems and a brief explanation of the method is given.

The general theory can lead to quite advanced work, either on the theoretical development or on its application to practical problems. Many of the ideas and methods presented are, however, quite simple and can be applied with advantage to the elementary teaching of electrical machine theory. The book should therefore be of interest to teachers in universities and technical colleges, and may, it is hoped, help them in their task of presenting a consistent and uniform treatment of all the different types of machine.

I wish to thank the Directors of the British Thomson-Houston Company and the Governors of Imperial College for permission to publish this book, and to acknowledge with thanks the help of many colleagues in its preparation. In particular I am greatly indebted to R. A. Hayes, M.A., former Fellow of Trinity Hall, Cambridge, who gave the text a most painstaking scrutiny from the point of view of clarity and accuracy of presentation, and to W. J. Gibbs, D.Sc., M.I.E.E., for many valuable suggestions of a general nature. The sections relating to power system analysis were checked by M. W. Humphrey Davies, M.Sc., M.I.E.E. Professor of Electrical Engineering, Queen Mary College.

BERNARD ADKINS

South Kensington,
*April 1955.*

# CONTENTS

Page

*Introduction*                                                    1

Chapter

*I. The Basis of the General Theory*                              7

   1. The Idealised Machine.

   2. The Two-winding Transformer. Explanation of Sign Conventions and the Per-unit System.

   3. Magneto-motive Force and Flux in the Rotating Machine.

   4. The Fundamental Assumptions. Saturation, Harmonics, Leakage.

*II. Methods of Analysis of Machines*                            27

   5. The Voltage and Torque Equations. Matrix Notation.

   6. Types of Problem and Methods of Solution.

   7. Representation of Sinusoidal Quantities by Harmonic Vectors and Complex Numbers.

   8. The Heaviside Operational Method.

   9. Analysers and Computers for Electrical Machine Problems.

*III. The D.C. Machine*                                          53

   10. The Equations of the D.C. Machine.

   11. Interpole, Compensating and Series Windings.

   12. Equations for Small Changes or Small Oscillations.

   13. Sudden Short-circuit of a D.C. Generator.

*IV. D.C. Machines in Control Systems*                           74

   14. The D.C. Generator as an Amplifier.

   15. Cross-field Generators.

   16. D.C. Motors in Control Systems.

   17. The Analysis of Control Systems.

CONTENTS

*Chapter*                                                        *Page*

*V. The Steady-state Vector Diagrams of A.C. Machines*    86

    18. Representation of Sinusoidal M.M.F. and Flux Waves by Space Vectors.

    19. The Induction Motor.

    20. The Cylindrical-rotor Synchronous Machine.

    21. The Salient-pole Synchronous Machine.

    22. The Power-angle Characteristic of a Synchronous Machine.

*VI. General Equations for A.C. Machines*    101

    23. Transformation Formulae for a Rotating Three-phase Winding.

    24. General Equations of the Synchronous Machine.

    25. Simplified Equations of a Synchronous Machine with Two Damper Coils.

    26. General Equations of the Induction Motor.

    27. Application of the Equations to A.C. Machine Problems.

*VII. A.C. Operation of Synchronous and Induction Machines*    132

    28. Steady Operation of the Synchronous Machine at Synchronous Speed.

    29. Starting Conditions of A.C. Motors.

    30. The Torque-speed Curve of the Synchronous Motor.

    31. The Negative-sequence Reactances of a Synchronous Machine.

*VIII. Symmetrical Short Circuit of an Alternator*    145

    32. Short Circuit of an Unloaded Alternator.

    33. The Analysis of Short-circuit Oscillograms.

    34. Short Circuit or Sudden Change of Voltage on a Loaded Alternator.

*IX. Synchronising Phenomena and Sustained Oscillations in Synchronous Machines*    159

    35. General Equations for Operation near to Synchronous Speed.

    36. The Synchronising Problem.

    37. Forced Oscillations and Free Oscillations.

    38. Calculation of the Elastic and Damping Constants.

# CONTENTS

*Chapter*                                                    *Page*

**X.** *Approximate Methods for Generator and System Analysis*                                              **174**

    39. The Problems of Power-system Analysis.

    40. Equivalent Circuits and Vector Diagrams for Approximate Calculations.

    41. The Analysis of Unbalanced Conditions.

    42. Application of the Approximate Methods to Power-system Analysis.

**XI.** *The Generalised Rotating Machine*                    **201**

    43. Matrix Transformations.

    44. Applications of the Generalised Equations of a Machine with Three Coils.

    45. Steady-state Equations of the Polyphase Induction Motor and the Schrage Motor.

    46. The Equations of Interconnected Systems.

*Chronological Bibliography*                                  **230**

*Index*                                                      **234**

# INTRODUCTION

THE PURPOSE of this book is to present a general theory of rotating electrical machines, applicable to all the normal types of machine and to all conditions of operation, and consequently more fundamental and of wider application than the usual theories given in the standard textbooks. The theory applies to all machines in which alternate magnetic poles are formed round a cylindrical surface, except that it is not applicable to the special machines of the inductor type in which there are salient poles on both fixed and moving elements.

An analytical study of electrical machines consists of two parts:

1. Determination of the basic characteristics expressed by a number of quantities known as the 'machine constants'.

2. Calculation from the constants of the performance of the machine under given external conditions.

The term 'Theory of electrical machines', as interpreted in this book, refers only to the second part. The theory starts with an idealised machine, the properties of which are expressed by known constants, and provides a means of calculating its performance. For the purposes of the theory, the constants, which are essentially resistances and inductances, must be carefully defined, but the methods of calculating them, with which the first of the above two parts is concerned, although very important for practical design work, form a separate subject.

In the usual textbook theories of electrical machines each type of machine is dealt with on its own merits without very much reference to other types, and simple methods of analysis are developed by means of which the performance under specified conditions can be calculated. In these theories the main emphasis is on steady operation, and they lead to graphical or analytical methods of calculation. For A.C. machines, vector diagrams are very widely used. This standard approach has the disadvantage that a completely fresh start has to be made when it is necessary to analyse a new type of machine or to deal with unbalanced or transient conditions.

1

It is interesting to survey the historical development of the theory of electrical machines. The early theories of A.C. machines were based on the vector diagram and were worked out by geometrical constructions on a drawing-board. There followed a search for equivalent circuits, which finally led to the acceptance of a few standard circuits selected from a large number of possible ones. The next important development was the introduction of complex numbers in what was known as the 'symbolic method' or the '$j$-method'. At that time, however, the algebraic method was not introduced in its own right, but only as an auxiliary process to assist in working out the vector diagrams or equivalent circuits. The modern methods involve a new approach to the subject. In the modern theory the algebraic equations are accepted as the fundamental means of expression, and vector diagrams and equivalent circuits become merely devices leading to alternative methods of solution applicable only to special cases. The use of equations is in line with recent developments in circuit theory, and leads to a general theory of electrical machines which embraces all types and all conditions of operation.

The fundamental set of equations is derived for an idealised two-pole machine, which is approximately equivalent to the actual machine, in accordance with certain well-defined assumptions. In general they are differential equations in which an applied voltage is equated to the sum of several component voltages which depend on the currents, or an applied torque is equated to component torques. In D.C. machines the equations relating the actual currents with the voltages and torque are usually in a convenient form for practical solution, but for most problems in A.C. machines the equations tend to be complicated and difficult to solve. The equations for A.C. machines become considerably simpler if they are expressed in terms of certain fictitious currents and voltages, which are different from but are related to the actual ones. The fictitious currents can have a physical meaning in that they can be considered to flow in fictitious windings acting along two axes at right angles, called the direct and quadrature axes. In this way a 'two-axis theory' of A.C. machines is developed, and the equations so obtained are found to correspond very closely to those of D.C. machines.

By co-ordinating the equations of different types of machine, a generalised theory, applicable to all types of electrical machine, is derived.

The essential point of the modern general theory, in comparison with earlier methods, is therefore that it is expressed in terms of equations. In the author's view this point is much more important than the subsidiary question whether matrices or tensors are used for expressing or manipulating the equations. In practical work, matrix methods are often extremely useful for organising the algebraic and arithmetical work, and tensors are of great value for more advanced theoretical investigations. Nevertheless, for the present purpose, both matrices and tensors should be regarded as mathematical tools, applied to a fundamental concept which can be completely, although less elegantly, expressed in terms of ordinary algebra.

The first step towards the development of a generalised theory was Blondel's 'two-reaction theory' of the steady-state operation of the salient-pole synchronous machine. The method was examined in detail by Doherty and Nickle, who published a series of five important papers (Refs. 26.2, 26.3, 27.1, 28.1 and 30.2).* A paper by West on "The Cross-field Theory of Alternating Current Machines" (Ref. 26.1) assumed without proof that a rotating squirrel-cage winding is equivalent to a D.C. armature winding with two short-circuited pairs of brushes. A very valuable contribution to the subject was made by Park in a set of three papers (Refs. 28.2, 29.1 and 33.2). These papers not only develop the general two-axis equations of the synchronous machine, but they indicate how the equations can be applied to many important practical problems. Park's transformation provides the most important fundamental concept in the development of Kron's generalised theory, which was first published in a series of papers in *The General Electric Review* (Ref. 35.1), and later in a book (Ref. 42.1).

During the last twenty years many papers dealing with particular problems, some of which are referred to in the bibliography, have appeared. Many of the important results are included in two books by Concordia (Ref. 51.1) and Laible (Ref. 51.2).

* The references are arranged in chronological order and the reference numbers refer to the *year* of publication. See Bibliography page 230.

Gibbs has published a paper on the application of matrices to machine theory (Ref. 51.6) and a book on the application of tensors (Ref. 52.1).

In the present book there are two introductory chapters (Chaps. I and II), followed by two on D.C. machines (Chaps. III and IV) and six on A.C. machines (Chaps. V to X). In these chapters the general equations are derived and used for solving a wide range of practical problems. The main purpose is to give a full explanation of the theory and to demonstrate its wide range of application. There is no attempt to give a comprehensive treatment, but references are given to assist any reader who wishes to pursue the matter further. In Chap. XI a statement of the generalised theory is given in matrix notation, and some of the simpler methods of matrix algebra are explained.

The general equations provide a means by which almost any possible problem in the operation of electrical machines can be investigated, although the solution of any given practical problem by the methods indicated may require difficult mathematics and lengthy numerical calculations. Not all problems can be solved exactly, and for those that can the computation of the solution may be too laborious. A good deal of attention has therefore been paid, on the one hand, to the development of approximate methods, and on the other to the use of analysers and computing devices. There is much scope for further work on the analysis of machine and power-system problems on these lines.

### Terminology and Notation

The terminology and notation used in developing the general theory follows in most respects that used in the papers and books listed in the bibliography. The symbols and names used for the constants of the synchronous machine, for example, are very well established, and are adhered to except for the minor changes mentioned on page 124. The sign conventions, as explained on page 16, are those used by Kron.

For A.C. problems vectors and complex numbers are used, but the approach is algebraic, instead of the usual geometrical one (see Sect. 7). The importance of using a different symbol for a vector or complex number representing a sinusoidal quantity from that used for the instantaneous value is stressed. The term 'vector' is used rather than alternative terms like 'phasor' (Ref. 51.4), since it is held that the vector representing a sinusoidal quantity is a genuine two-dimensional vector, which must, however, be distinguished from the three-dimensional 'field vector' representing a physical property of a point in space.

In the differential equations, the Heaviside notation is used, as explained in Sect. 8. The Heaviside notation is used by Kron and many other writers on electrical machine theory, but it has been suggested (Ref. 51.2) that it would be preferable to employ the more rigorous Laplace transform method for the equations of machines, as is now most often done in writings dealing with the theory of circuits or of automatic control systems. In the author's view, it is advantageous to use the Heaviside notation for the general equations of machines because of the fact that they are non-linear. The Laplace transform notation is suitable for the study of circuits and control systems because, for these subjects, the equations used in developing the basic theory are linear.

The presentation of the theory of electrical machines can be divided into two parts:

(a) Statement and manipulation of the equations.

(b) Solution of the equations.

The Heaviside method is very convenient for stating the equations even when they are non-linear. It can moreover be used for manipulating the equations under certain conditions, for example, when some are linear and some are non-linear as in the problem of Sect. 36. Laplace transforms cannot be used for this purpose. For those problems for which the equations are linear (for example, the short-circuit problems of Sects. 13 or 31) either the Heaviside method or the Laplace transform method could be used both for the statement and the solution, and the two methods are in fact equivalent.

Thus the present book uses the Heaviside method throughout, following Kron's notation (Ref. 42.1), apart from one minor change; viz., that the symbol $\nu$ is used for the speed in preference to $p\theta$. Although, in Kron's work, it is understood that $p\theta$ is always to be considered as a single variable, the notation is confusing and the use of a single symbol makes for greater clarity.

### The Per-unit System

In most of the equations in the book a normalised system of units, known as the per-unit system, is used for the voltages, currents and other quantities. The voltages and currents in the main, or primary, circuits are expressed as fractions of the nominal values, which are taken to be the unit values as explained on page 17. For other mutually coupled circuits, unit current is that which produces the same M.M.F. as the primary unit current and unit voltage is induced by the same flux as the primary unit voltage.

The units of power, torque and other mechanical quantities are defined on page 32. The unit of time is the second and the unit of speed is the radian per second. In this respect the units differ from those in some of the literature, where a unit of time which makes the nominal speed equal to unity is used. It is held that there is little benefit in using this rather artificial unit of time, which brings about a confusion between inductance and reactance.

CHAPTER 1

# The Basis of the General Theory

## 1. The Idealised Machine

All types of rotating electrical machine have many common features, as illustrated in Fig. 1. In the typical arrangement shown, there is an outer stationary member and an inner rotating member mounted in bearings fixed to the stationary member. The two elements carry cylindrical iron cores separated by an air-gap, and a common magnetic flux $\Phi$ passes across

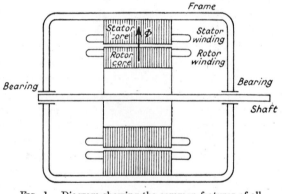

FIG. 1.—Diagram showing the common features of all electrical machines.

the air-gap from one core to the other in a combined magnetic circuit. Very occasionally the inner member is fixed while the outer member rotates, or, in other special cases, both elements may rotate. The important feature of all machines is that two cylindrical iron surfaces, a short distance apart, move relatively to one another. The cylindrical surface on either element may be virtually continuous, broken only by small slot openings uniformly spaced round the circle, or it may be divided into an even number of salient poles with spaces between them.

Near the surface of each element, conductors carrying currents

7

run parallel to the axis of the cylinders. The conductors are connected into coils by end connections outside the core, and the coils are connected to form the machine windings, which, on either element, consist of a relatively small number of circuits carrying independent currents. The operation of the machine depends primarily on the distribution of the currents round the core surfaces, and the analysis of the windings is concerned only with this distribution. The detailed arrangement of the end connections is of secondary importance.

Thus the general arrangement is the same for all types of machine. The various types differ fundamentally only in the distribution of the conductors forming the windings and in whether the elements have continuous cores or salient poles. The operation of any given machine depends also on the nature of the voltages applied to its windings.

The narrow annular space between the two elements, known as the *air-gap*, is the critical region of the machine, and the theory is mainly concerned with the conditions in or near the air-gap. The magnetic flux is actually distributed in a very complicated manner throughout the iron core, but, because of the high permeability of the iron, a reasonably simple and accurate theory can be derived by considering only the flux distribution in or near the air-gap. The conductors are actually located, not in the air-gap itself, but near to it. They are placed either in slots formed in the laminations of which the core is built or in the interpolar space between salient poles. Nevertheless, the theory is developed by replacing the actual conductors by equivalent conductors (usually assumed to be of small size) located at the surface of the core. The secondary factors not covered by these assumptions are dealt with under the heading of 'leakage', which is discussed in some detail in later sections.

The essential arrangement of the machine can thus be represented on a drawing of a section perpendicular to the axis of the cores. The two-dimensional drawing can then be further simplified to a *developed diagram* showing the air-gap surface developed along a straight line. Fig. 2(a) shows, as an example, a sectional drawing of a six-pole machine having salient poles on the outer member and a continuous core on the inner member. Fig. 2(b) shows the corresponding developed diagram.

Because the radial length of the air-gap is small, it is permissible as an approximation to represent the path round the air-gap as a straight line in the developed diagram, and to speak of a definite value of flux density at any point on this

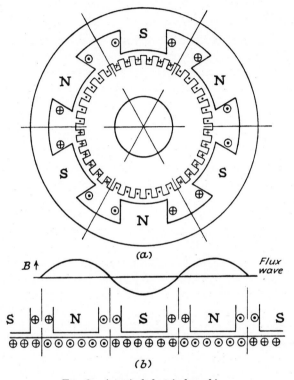

FIG. 2.—A typical electrical machine.
(a) Sectional drawing. (b) Developed diagram.

line. The currents are usually assumed to be concentrated at the points on the air-gap line corresponding either to the centre of a slot opening or to the edge of a salient pole.

In the developed diagram the distribution of flux and current repeats itself every two poles, whatever the actual number of poles may be. (Slight variations due to fractional-slot windings or staggered poles are ignored in working out the theory.) Hence any machine can be replaced by an equivalent two-pole machine and only such machines need be considered. In this book the theory is developed entirely in terms of two-pole machines. The number of poles must of course be introduced in determining the constants of the machine, particularly when considering mechanical quantities such as torque and speed.

## Types of Winding

The windings of electrical machines are of three main types:

1. *Coil winding*. The winding consists of coils similarly placed on all poles, and connected together by series or parallel connection into a single circuit. Usually the coils are wound round salient poles as indicated in Fig. 2, but sometimes, as in a turbo-alternator field winding, a coil winding may lie in slots.

2. *Polyphase winding*. The individual conductors are distributed in slots and are connected into several separate circuits, one for each phase. The groups of conductors forming the phase bands are distributed in regular sequence over successive pole pitches.

3. *Commutator winding*. The conductors are located in slots and are connected to commutator segments in a continuous sequence. The current flows from the external circuit into and out of the winding through brushes pressing on the commutator surface. Depending on the arrangement of the brush-gear, there may be only one external circuit, or there may be more than one external circuit.

The type of machine depends on what combination of these types of winding is used on the stator and rotor; for example, a D.C. machine has a coil winding and a commutator winding, a synchronous machine has a coil winding and a polyphase winding, and an induction motor has two polyphase windings. The first two types of winding may be on either the stationary member or the rotating member of the machine, but a commutator winding with stationary brushes must necessarily be on the rotating member.

The above classification is clearly not a rigid one. For example, a single-phase A.C. winding can be treated alternatively as a special case of a polyphase winding or as a coil winding. A uniform squirrel cage, though not strictly a polyphase winding with independent circuits, can usually be replaced by one. An

10

irregular squirrel cage on a synchronous machine, on the other hand, must be treated as a number of separate coil windings.

## The idealised two-pole machine

For any type of machine the theory is developed for an *idealised two-pole machine*, which is approximately equivalent to the actual machine. Each winding of the actual machine, or each part of a winding forming a single circuit, is represented

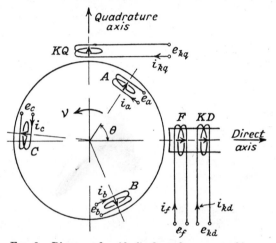

Fig. 3.—Diagram of an idealised synchronous machine.

in the idealised machine by a single coil. For the purpose of analysis it is immaterial which of the two elements of the machine rotates and which is stationary, since its operation depends only on the relative motion between them. In a practical machine with salient poles, for example, either element may carry the salient poles. It is, however, convenient when representing such a machine by an idealised two-pole machine to take the salient-pole element to be stationary and to indicate it on the diagram as the outer member. For a machine with a commutator, the commutator winding is always on the rotor, and the element carrying it is always indicated on the diagram of the idealised machine as the inner rotating member.

As an example, an idealised three-phase salient-pole synchronous machine is shown in Fig. 3. A practical machine of this type usually has its three-phase armature winding on the stator and the field winding on the rotor, but machines with the reverse arrangement are often built. The type is represented in Fig. 3 as having salient poles on the outer stationary member, although it is understood that the theory applies to either arrangement. Only one of the two salient poles is indicated. The stator carries a field coil $F$ and damper coils $KD$ and $KQ$. The axis of the pole round which the field coil $F$ is wound is called the *direct axis* of the machine, while the axis 90° away from it is called the *quadrature axis*. At the instant considered, the axis of the coil representing the armature phase $A$ makes an angle $\theta$ in a counter-clockwise direction with the direct axis. The instantaneous angular speed is indicated by the Greek letter $v$.

The positive direction of the current in any coil is towards the coil in the lead nearer to the centre of the diagram, as indicated by an arrow in Fig. 3. The positive direction of the flux linking a coil is radially outwards, as indicated by an arrow-head along the axis in the middle of the loop representing the coil. The loops of the coils are not intended to show the direction round the pole, but the convention is adopted that a current in a positive direction in a coil on any axis sets up a flux in the positive direction of that axis.

In referring to the diagrams of idealised machines, such as Fig. 3, the term *coil* is used to indicate a part of the complete winding which forms a single circuit and carries a single current. In the actual machine such a coil may consist of many turns, distributed over many poles and often in several slots on each pole, but it is represented in the idealised machine by a single coil. The term *winding*, on the other hand, may refer to a single coil—for example, the field coil $F$—or it may refer to several coils, as in the three-phase armature winding represented by the three coils $A$, $B$ and $C$. Often it is necessary to make approximations. The squirrel-cage damper winding of a synchronous machine consists in practice of many circuits carrying different currents and would require a large number of coils for its exact representation. For many practical purposes it is sufficiently accurate to represent the damper winding by only two coils $KD$ and $KQ$, as in Fig. 3, which affords an example of the kind of approximation that is necessary in order to obtain a workable theory.

As a second example, Fig. 4 is the diagram of an idealised cross-field direct-current machine having salient poles on the stator and a commutator winding with main brushes on the direct axis and cross brushes on the quadrature axis. In the diagrams of commutator machines the convention is adopted

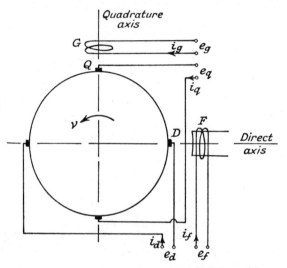

FIG. 4.—Diagram of an idealised cross-field D.C. machine.

that a brush is shown at the position occupied by the armature conductor to which the segment under the brush is connected. The circuits through the brushes are labelled $D$ and $Q$ respectively. The machine represented also has a main field winding $F$ and a quadrature field winding $G$ acting along the direct and quadrature axes respectively. The machine may be represented alternatively by the four coils of Fig. 5, corresponding to the four separate circuits of Fig. 4.

The general theory of electrical machines given hereafter is developed for a generalised machine having a number of coils with their axes located on the fixed direct and quadrature axes. Fig. 5 shows the diagram of a generalised machine with one coil on each axis on each element, viz., $F$ and $G$ on the stationary member and $D$ and $Q$ on the rotating member. Some machines may require fewer than four coils to represent them, while others may require more. Any machine, however, can be shown to be equivalent to a generalised machine with an appropriate number of coils on each fixed axis. If the coils of the actual machine are permanently located on the axes, they correspond exactly to those of the generalised machine, but, if they are not, it is necessary to make a conversion. The process of conversion

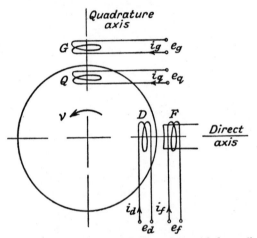

Fig. 5.—Diagram of a generalised machine with four coils.

from the actual coils of the machine itself to the equivalent axis coils of the corresponding generalised machine, or vice versa, is known as a *transformation*.

In order that the effects of rotation in an actual machine may be representable in an 'equivalent' generalised machine, it is necessary, as shown later, that the coils $D$ and $Q$ representing the winding on the moving element of the generalised machine should be considered to possess special properties. The properties are the same as those possessed by a commutator winding, in which the current passes between a pair of brushes, viz.:

1. A current in the coil produces a field which is stationary in space.
2. Nevertheless a voltage can be induced in the coil by rotation of the moving element.

14

Such a coil, located on a moving element but with its axis stationary, and so possessing the above two properties, may be termed a *pseudo-stationary coil*.

In the D.C. machine of Fig. 4, the actual circuits $D$ and $Q$ through the commutator winding not only form pseudo-stationary coils like the coils $D$ and $Q$ of the generalised machine of Fig. 5, but have the same axes as these coils. There is thus an exact correspondence between Figs. 4 and 5, and as a result the generalised equations derived for the generalised machine of Fig. 5 apply directly to the D.C. machine of Fig. 4. On the other hand, the three moving coils on the armature of the synchronous machine of Fig. 3 do not directly correspond to the coils $D$ and $Q$ of Fig. 5. In developing the general two-axis theory of the synchronous machine, the three-phase coils $A$, $B$ and $C$ are replaced by equivalent axis coils $D$ and $Q$, like those of Fig. 5. The transformation involved in the conversion, which depends on the fact that the same M.M.F. is set up in the machine by either system, is explained and justified in Sect. 23.

In applying the generalised theory to any type of rotating electrical machine the process may be summarised as follows. The diagram of the idealised two-pole machine is first set out using the smallest number of coils required to obtain a result of sufficient accuracy. The idealised two-pole machine is then related to a generalised machine with an appropriate number of coils, either directly or by means of suitable transformations. The theory is developed by deriving a set of voltage equations relating the voltages and currents of the generalised machine and, in addition, a torque equation relating the torque to the currents. The speed appears as a variable in the equations.

## 2. The Two-winding Transformer. Explanation of Sign Conventions and the Per-unit System

The process of idealisation described in Sect. 1 reduces the machine to a set of mutually coupled coils, which, however, differ from normal mutually coupled coils because of the special property assigned to the coils on the rotating member. A machine, in fact, differs from a static transformer because of its rotation. A consideration of the simpler apparatus is, however, valuable as a starting-point, and in this section the two-winding transformer is used to explain several of the important concepts in the treatment of the rotating machine.

Consider the system of two mutually coupled coils illustrated in Fig. 6. Each coil is assumed to be *concentrated*, that is, its turns are wound closely together so that the same flux links every turn. A current in either coil flowing in the direction shown sets up a flux in the direction indicated by the heavy arrow.

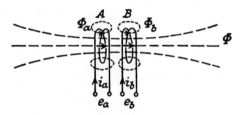

Fig. 6.—Diagram of a transformer.

*Main flux and leakage flux*

The flux in the transformer can be split up into three parts:

(a) *Main flux* $\Phi$ linking both coils.
(b) *Primary leakage flux* $\Phi_a$, due to current $i_a$, and linking coil A but not coil B.
(c) *Secondary leakage flux* $\Phi_b$, due to current $i_b$, and linking coil B but not coil A.

This statement embodies the fundamental definition of the leakage flux of one coil in relation to another, viz., that it is the flux, due to the current in the one coil, which links that coil but not the other.

*Symbols and sign conventions*

In all the diagrams of idealised machines in this book the coils are indicated by letters, which are used as suffixes to distinguish voltages, currents and other quantities. In Fig. 6 the letters A and B are used for the primary and secondary coils of the transformer.

The sign convention adopted for voltages and currents is as follows:

$e$ represents the voltage impressed on the coil from an external source;

$i$ represents the current measured in the same direction as $e$.

With the above convention, the instantaneous power $ei$ flows into the circuit from outside, if both $e$ and $i$ are positive.

In a general theory covering both motors and generators it is important to use the same sign convention throughout. The convention adopted corresponds directly to motor operation and introduces negative quantities for generator operation. It agrees with the usual convention of circuit theory and has the advantage of introducing the minimum number of negative signs in the equations. It differs from the convention used by Park, who was concerned primarily with the synchronous generator, and agrees with that used by Kron, whose aim was to treat all the machines on a common basis.

To take a simple example, the equation for a circuit with resistance $r$ and inductance $L$ is:

$$e = ri + L\frac{di}{dt}.$$

In the equations in this book the symbol $p$ is used for the operator $\frac{d}{dt}$ so that the above equation can be written:

$$e = (r + Lp)i. \qquad \ldots(1.1)$$

In the derivation of the equations this may be regarded just as an abbreviation, but in later sections the notation is used in solving the equations by Heaviside's operational method.

### The per-unit system

In developing the theories of electrical machines and power systems it is advantageous in many ways to measure the quantities, not in the usual units but on a *per-unit system*. To apply the per-unit system to the transformer of Fig. 6, the *units of primary voltage and current* are chosen arbitrarily, generally as the nominal rated values. The *per-unit value* of voltage or

17

current in the coil is then the number of these units in the actual value; for example, if the voltage is a half of rated voltage, $e = 0.5$ per-unit.

The units for the secondary quantities are related to the primary units. If the ratio of the secondary turns to primary turns is $N$, the *unit of secondary voltage* is $N$ times the unit of primary voltage, and the *unit of secondary current* is $1/N$ times the unit of primary current.

The *unit of flux* is defined to be such that unit rate of change of flux induces unit voltage in *either* coil (time in seconds).

The *units of inductance* are such that

$$\Phi = M_{ab}(i_a + i_b),$$
$$\Phi_a = l_a i_a,$$
$$\Phi_b = l_b i_b,$$

where $M_{ab}$ is the *mutual inductance* and $l_a$ and $l_b$ are the *leakage inductances*.

Unit resistance for *either* coil is such that unit current produces unit voltage drop.

The induced voltage in coil $A$ is:

$$-\frac{d}{dt}(\Phi + \Phi_a).$$

The impressed voltage is in the opposite sense to the induced voltage. The value of the impressed voltage on coil $A$ is:

$$e_a = r_a i_a + (M_{ab} + l_a)\frac{di_a}{dt} + M_{ab}\frac{di_b}{dt}.$$

There is a similar equation for the secondary coil. Using the symbol $p$ for $\frac{d}{dt}$, the two equations of the transformer are:

$$\left. \begin{aligned} e_a &= \{r_a + (M_{ab} + l_a)p\}i_a + \qquad\quad M_{ab}pi_b \\ e_b &= \qquad\quad M_{ab}pi_a \qquad\quad + \{r_b + (M_{ab} + l_b)p\}i_b \end{aligned} \right\} \quad \dots(1.2)$$

*Complete inductance and leakage inductance*

The term inductance, when applied to machines and transformers, is often used in two different senses. Strictly, the inductance of a coil is given by the voltage induced by the total flux set up when the rate of change of current in the coil is unity. Applied to the primary coil $A$ this inductance would correspond to flux $(\Phi+\Phi_a)$ when the secondary winding carries no current ($i_b=0$). It is called the *complete inductance* and is represented by the symbol $L_a$. On the other hand, the leakage inductance $l_a$, which in practical work is often called 'the inductance of the primary winding' is much smaller than the complete inductance, and corresponds only to the leakage flux $\Phi_a$.

It is important to distinguish clearly between complete and leakage inductances. In this book complete inductance is denoted by the capital letter $L$, and leakage inductance by the small letter $l$. In the two-winding transformer, *if a per-unit system is used*, the complete inductance of either winding is the sum of the mutual inductance and the leakage inductance.

$$\left.\begin{aligned} L_a &= M_{ab}+l_a \\ L_b &= M_{ab}+l_b \end{aligned}\right\}. \qquad \text{...(1.3)}$$

Eqns. (1.2) can then be written:

$$\left.\begin{aligned} e_a &= (r_a+L_a p)i_a + M_{ab}p i_b \\ e_b &= \quad M_{ab}p i_a \; + (r_b+L_b p)i_b \end{aligned}\right\}. \qquad \text{...(1.4)}$$

*Advantages of the per-unit system*

The per-unit system is of great benefit in making design calculations for machines, because it makes the comparison between different machines very much easier. Corresponding quantities are of the same order of magnitude even for widely different designs.

In the formulation of the theory the per-unit system has the great merit that the numbers of turns do not enter into the equations. Moreover the very useful relation, stated in Eqns. (1.3), that the complete inductance of a coil is obtained by adding the mutual and leakage inductances, would not be true if the quantities were expressed in normal units.

### 3. Magneto-motive Force and Flux in the Rotating Machine

In any machine the currents in all the windings combine together to produce the resultant flux. The action of the machine depends on the facts, firstly, that the flux induces voltages in the windings, and, secondly, that the flux interacts with the currents to produce torque.

### Main air-gap flux

The flux spreads throughout the whole machine, but its effect depends primarily on the distribution of flux density round the air-gap; the attention is therefore focused on this region. At any instant the curve of flux density round the air-gap may be of any form and is not necessarily sinusoidal. The *main flux* of the machine is for many purposes considered to be determined by the fundamental component of the curve of flux density, and the radial line where the fundamental density is a maximum is called the *axis of the flux*. The main flux is then completely defined by a magnitude and a direction.

### Magneto-motive force

In order to calculate the flux due to a given system of currents it is first necessary to determine the magneto-motive force (M.M.F.) due to the currents. Fig. 7 is a developed diagram

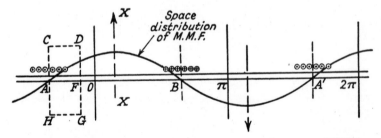

Fig. 7.—Developed diagram showing the distribution of current and M.M.F.

for a two-pole machine extending between angular positions $O$ and $2\pi$. The currents in the conductors of a coil are distributed in slots as indicated and form two bands, symmetrically distributed about the points $A$ and $B$. The currents in the two bands flow in opposite directions. Since the current distribution is known, the M.M.F. round any closed path can be found; in particular, the M.M.F. round a path crossing the air-gap, such as $ACDFGH$. Because of the high permeability of the iron, all the M.M.F. round the closed path can be assumed to be concentrated at the air-gap at the point $F$, if $A$ is chosen as a point of zero air-gap flux density, which, for a symmetrical distribution of current, must occur at the centre of each band. Hence a curve of M.M.F. distribution round the air-gap can be drawn for any value of current flowing in the coil. Thus, although magneto-motive force is fundamentally a line integral round a closed path, a value can be associated with each point on the air-gap line, giving *the M.M.F. curve* of the machine. If the conductors are assumed to be located at points along the air-gap line, the M.M.F. curve is a stepped curve, but the fundamental component, which, by symmetry, is zero at the points $A$ and $B$, can be drawn as in Fig. 7. The radial line at the point of maximum M.M.F. ($XX$ in Fig. 7) is called the *axis of the M.M.F.*, and since this depends only on the conductor distribution, it is also the *axis of the coil*. The curve shows the instantaneous magnitude of the M.M.F., which depends on the instantaneous value of the current.

The M.M.F. curve determines the flux density curve. If the machine has a uniform air-gap, and if saturation is neglected, the flux density is everywhere proportional to the M.M.F. In a salient-pole machine, however, this is no longer true, and, in order to calculate the flux, it becomes necessary to resolve the M.M.F. wave into component waves along the direct and quadrature axes. On either axis a sinusoidal M.M.F. wave produces a flux density distribution, which can be determined by flux plotting or by other well-known methods. The flux density curve is not sinusoidal, but because of the symmetry of the pole about its axis, its fundamental component has the same axis as the M.M.F. producing it. Hence, if the harmonics are ignored, an M.M.F. wave on either the direct or quadrature axis produces a proportional sinusoidal flux wave on the same axis, the factors of proportionality being different for the two axes. By this means the flux components on the two axes, due to any current, can be found and, if there is no saturation, the resultant flux wave is obtained by combining them.

### 4. The Fundamental Assumptions. Saturation, Harmonics, Leakage

The assumptions made in the last section are based on those given by Park (Ref. 28.2). The principal assumptions are that there is no saturation and that space harmonics in the flux wave may be neglected. Before proceeding with the theory, it is worth while to examine what is involved.

*Saturation and other non-linear effects*

In the idealised machine it is assumed that all voltages are proportional to the currents producing them; that is, that there are no saturation or other non-linear effects. Now in practice saturation is an extremely important factor, and much ingenuity has been used in devising methods of taking it into account. These methods occupy a large part in any textbook on electrical machine design; for example, the treatment of armature reaction in a D.C. machine, or the use of 'Potier reactance' in a synchronous machine. Such methods do not, however, introduce the non-linear property into the basic theory. They are directed mainly to the determination of appropriate values of constants to suit the particular problem, the constants being defined in relation to a linear theory.

The fundamental theory must of necessity be based on linear relationships, because a theory which allowed directly for non-linear effects would be quite impracticable, and it is important that the practical adjustments should not be allowed to obscure the fundamental background of the theoretical analysis. The present book is primarily concerned with the development of the linear theory.

In applying the theory to practical problems the effect of saturation must always be borne in mind, since the accuracy of the final result depends on the skill with which the constants are chosen. Because of the uncertainty introduced by the presence of saturation it is more than ever important to verify the results obtained, whenever possible, by tests on actual machines, so as to develop empirical methods of determining the appropriate constants (see Ref. 35.2).

With the assumption of linearity the *principle of superposition* can be used. The current in any coil sets up a magneto-motive force and hence a component of flux, which may induce a voltage in the coil itself or in any other coil. By the principle of superposition all the component voltages in any coil can be added together to obtain the resultant voltage. Using Kirchhoff's Law, which states that the sum of all the voltages in a circuit is equal to the voltage impressed on it from outside, a voltage equation is obtained for each of the coils of the machine. The voltage equations for all the coils, together with a torque equation, constitute the *general equations of the machine,* which determine completely its operation when the applied voltages and torque are known.

*Harmonics*

The neglect of space harmonics in the general theory, although convenient for giving a simple explanation, is actually a good deal more drastic than is necessary, because the effect of many harmonics can be included by modifying the values of the main and leakage inductances. When the machine is at rest, all the space harmonics in the flux wave can be allowed for in this way, since it is then in effect a static transformer. When the machine rotates some of the voltages due to harmonics would require additional, and usually more complicated, terms in the equations, and it is these harmonics that are neglected.

Consider first a machine operating with alternating current under steady conditions. The vector diagram for any particular circuit can only include voltages of a single frequency. Any space harmonics which induce voltages of this frequency can therefore be allowed for in the theory, while those which induce voltages of a different frequency must be neglected. The harmonics of the second group produce parasitic effects such as noise, voltage ripples, or parasitic torques, and it is important to make them as small as possible. A good deal of attention has been paid to this question, and a good design embodies many special features for the purpose of reducing undesirable harmonics. Such matters are outside the scope of this book, and it is assumed in the development of the general theory that these harmonics can be neglected.

The general equations of a machine apply to all possible manners of variation of the instantaneous values of current and

23

voltage, among which a sine wave alternation is only a special case. The flux harmonics, however, still fall into two groups, namely, those which induce voltages that can be included with the normal terms in the equation, and those which would require additional terms. It is only the harmonics of the second group that are neglected.

## Leakage

The greater part of the leakage flux in a machine, defined in the same way as for the transformer on page 16, arises because the conductors are located in slots instead of on the air-gap surface, and because the windings have end connections outside the core. Considering first a machine having only one winding on each element, the leakage flux round the slots does not cross the air-gap and consequently only links the winding which produces it. There is also the so-called *zigzag leakage* flux, which crosses the air-gap but does not penetrate far enough into the core to link the winding on the other side. The inductance corresponding to these types of leakage is quite definite and can be calculated by well-known methods.

In addition, as explained above, a winding produces harmonic fluxes which cross the air-gap and link the other winding, but are distinct from the main flux which has been defined as the fundamental part. In some instances the voltages induced by these harmonics can be usefully allowed for in the equations of the machine, and in others they cannot. For example, in an induction motor running under steady conditions, the voltage induced in one winding by a harmonic flux wave due to the other winding cannot be included in the equations because, owing to the relative motion of the windings, it has a different frequency from the voltage induced by the corresponding fundamental flux wave. Only in the winding producing the harmonic flux wave can the voltage induced by it be allowed for, when the effect of the harmonic is equivalent to an increase of leakage flux linked with the winding. The equivalent increase of leakage flux is known as *belt leakage*.

In a commutator machine, on the other hand, the commutator winding produces harmonic flux waves which are similar to those set up by a stator winding. Such harmonics normally

24

induce voltages in the stator of such a nature that they can be included in the equations, and consequently their effect is equivalent to an increase of the main flux.

It is therefore not true that all harmonics are neglected in the general theory, provided that the correct values of inductances are chosen. Those harmonics that are neglected can, however, cause considerable inaccuracy if the machine is not well designed. It is important to reduce the harmonics by correctly choosing the number and size of the slots, the pitch of the coils, and by other well-known precautions.

### Distributed windings

In the transformer discussed in Sect. 2, the coils are assumed to be concentrated and, as a result, there is a definite line of demarcation between main flux and leakage flux. If, on the other hand, the coils consist of turns distributed in space in different positions, there is no clear distinction between the two parts of the flux, because it is not possible to say what flux links both coils. It is necessary to assign arbitrarily a meaning to the term 'main flux' and to use an *effective number of turns* for each coil instead of the actual number of turns. According to the way in which the main flux is defined, there are different values of the mutual and leakage inductances and a different turn ratio.

In a rotating machine the windings are always distributed to some extent, and the main flux is defined as that corresponding to the fundamental sine wave component of the flux density curve. It is sometimes stated that the distinction between main and leakage flux in a machine is not definite. However, if the definition of the main flux as the sinusoidal component is adhered to, as in the present treatment, there is no ambiguity. The effective number of turns of a machine winding is determined, on the basis of a sinusoidal flux wave, by multiplying the actual number of turns by a *winding factor* which is calculated by well-known methods.

### Machines with more than two windings

The definition of leakage for any coil is made in particular relation to some other coil. Hence if there are three or more coils, any one has a different leakage flux in relation to each of the others. An accurate treatment in terms of leakage induct-ances therefore becomes complicated, and it is often preferable to set down the equations using complete self-inductances and mutual inductances.

In practice the concept of leakage can be applied in a simple manner to machines with three or more windings if some approximation is permissible. For example, if it is sufficiently accurate to assume that a common main flux links all the windings, a single leakage inductance for each winding and one common mutual inductance are all that are required.

# CHAPTER II

# *Methods of Analysis of Machines*

## 5. The Voltage and Torque Equations. Matrix Notation

*Steady and transient conditions*

The equations of the generalised machine can be used to determine the performance of any of the different types of machine under any condition of operation, steady or transient. Generally the applied voltages are known and it is required to determine the currents, while the torque and speed may be either known or unknown quantities. It is not feasible to obtain a general solution applicable to all conditions, and it is necessary to direct attention to particular problems.

The first important distinction is between transient and steady conditions. During a transient condition the voltages and currents, as well as torque and speed, are expressed as functions of time. The equations are differential equations and it is therefore necessary, for any particular problem, to know the initial conditions, or other boundary conditions, in order to obtain the solution. Steady conditions are of two types: D.C. conditions, when the quantities do not vary with time, and A.C. conditions, when the quantities vary sinusoidally with time. For steady conditions the general differential equations can be converted into algebraic equations, containing real or complex variables. In this chapter the different types of problem encountered in practice are classified under seven headings (see Table 1, page 36) and the methods available for their solution are discussed.

The conventional theories of electrical machines apply mainly to steady conditions, which are easier to deal with than the more general transient conditions. The steady-state theories are usually developed for particular machines, in terms of vector diagrams, equivalent circuits, and other devices, while transient conditions are considered quite independently. The general theory developed in this book embraces all these different conditions and shows the relation between the transient and steady conditions, as well as between the different types of machine.

## Matrix notation

Any set of simultaneous equations can be written in what is termed 'matrix' form by separating out the variables and coefficients. For example, Eqns. (1.4), when expressed in matrix form, become:

$$
\begin{array}{|c|}
\hline
e_a \\
\hline
e_b \\
\hline
\end{array}
=
\begin{array}{|c|c|}
\hline
r_a + L_a p & M_{ab} p \\
\hline
M_{ab} p & r_b + L_b p \\
\hline
\end{array}
\cdot
\begin{array}{|c|}
\hline
i_a \\
\hline
i_b \\
\hline
\end{array}
\qquad \ldots (2.1)
$$

Each array of numbers enclosed in a rectangular 'box' is called a *matrix*. In the above simple example, the *voltage matrix* and the *current matrix* each contain two compartments, while the *impedance matrix* contains four. In the general case, the voltage and current matrices would have $n$ and $m$ compartments respectively and the impedance matrix would have $mn$ compartments.

The first equation of Eqns. (1.4) is obtained from Eqns. (2.1) by multiplying each coefficient in the first horizontal row of the impedance matrix by the corresponding current in the vertical column of the current matrix, adding the terms together, and equating to the first element of the voltage matrix. The second equation is obtained by associating the second row of the impedance matrix with the current matrix in the same way. The notation is explained more fully on page 30.

In the first instance, the matrix notation can be regarded simply as an abbreviated method of writing the equations. Regarded in this way, the matrix notation has the advantage of setting out the equations in an orderly manner. In the main part of the book, the matrix notation is used only for this purpose, and the manipulation of the equations is carried out by ordinary algebraic methods.

There has been developed, however, a special technique of handling equations in matrix form. This subject is known as *matrix algebra* and is of great value in manipulating complicated equations. Some of the simpler methods of matrix algebra are explained and applied in Chap. XI.

*The general voltage equations*

The generalised machine of Fig. 5 has on each axis a pair of coils similar to the two coils of the transformer of Fig. 6. Since a stationary coil on one axis is mutually non-inductive with a stationary coil on the other axis, there would, if the machine were at rest, be no voltages induced in any coil on one axis due to currents in coils on the other axis. Hence the equations of each pair separately would be similar to those of the transformer. When the machine rotates, however, there are additional terms in the equations because, as a result of the rotation, voltages are induced in the pseudo-stationary coils $D$ and $Q$ by fluxes set up by currents on the other axis (see page 15).

For the D.C. machine of Fig. 4, or the alternative representation by four coils as shown in Fig. 5, the equations relating the voltages and currents in the four circuits can be shown to be as follows (see Sect. 10):

$$\left.\begin{aligned}
e_f &= (r_f + L_f p)i_f + M_{df}pi_d \\
e_d &= M_{df}pi_f + (r_d + L_d p)i_d + M_q v i_q + M_g v i_g \\
e_q &= -M_f v i_f - M_d v i_d + (r_q + L_q p)i_q + M_{qg}pi_g \\
e_g &= M_{qg}pi_q + (r_g + L_g p)i_g
\end{aligned}\right\}, \quad \ldots(2.2)$$

where the constants in the equations are resistances $r$, self-inductances $L$ and mutual inductances $M$, all with suffixes indicating the coils to which they refer. $M_{df}$ and $M_{qg}$ are analogous to the mutual inductance $M_{ab}$ in the transformer equations (1.4). $M_d$, $M_q$, $M_g$, $M_f$ are additional constants determining the voltage induced in an armature coil on one axis due to rotation in the flux produced by a current in a coil on the other axis.

The set of equations (2.2) may also be written in the form of a single matrix equation thus:

| $e_f$ | = | $r_f + L_f p$ | $M_{df}p$ | | | · | $i_f$ |
|-------|---|---------------|-----------|---|---|---|-------|
| $e_d$ | | $M_{df}p$ | $r_d + L_d p$ | $M_q v$ | $M_g v$ | | $i_d$ |
| $e_q$ | | $-M_f v$ | $-M_d v$ | $r_q + L_q p$ | $M_{qg}p$ | · | $i_q$ |
| $e_g$ | | | | $M_{qg}p$ | $r_g + L_g p$ | | $i_g$ |

$$\ldots(2.3)$$

The set of equations (2.2) can be read from the matrix equation (2.3) by equating the voltage in each row of the voltage matrix to the sum of the products of each successive coefficient in that row of the impedance matrix with the corresponding current in the vertical column of the current matrix. Thus, for example, the third impedance coefficient in the row (read from left to right) is multiplied by the third current in the column (read from top to bottom).

Each term of Eqns. (2.2) is obtained by determining the voltage induced in a particular circuit when current flows in one circuit only, in the same way as in ordinary circuit theory. The equation for any circuit is obtained by superimposing all the induced voltages and the resistance drop, and equating to the impressed voltage. The use of the matrix notation makes it easy to compare the different coefficients and shows at a glance which currents have zero coefficients.

In Eqns. (2.3) some terms contain the differential operator $p$, and represent voltages due to changing currents in coils on the same axis as the one being considered. They are called *transformer voltages*, and are present even when the machine is stationary. Other terms, containing the speed $v$, represent voltages induced by rotation in the flux set up by the current in a coil on the other axis. For example, $(-M_f v i_f)$ is the voltage induced between the quadrature-axis brushes by a current in the direct-axis field winding, and is the normal induced voltage in a simple D.C. machine consisting of circuits $Q$ and $F$ only. Such voltages are called *rotation voltages*. When the coils carry steady D.C. currents, there are no transformer voltages but the rotation voltages are still present.

With the conventions adopted on page 12, the signs of the rotation voltage terms are as shown in Eqns. (2.3). The sign of any rotation voltage can be determined by considering the torque produced by the interaction of the fields set up by the currents in the windings. A positive current $i_f$ sets up a flux passing outwards along the direct axis and hence a south pole on the surface of the stator pole, while a positive current $i_q$ sets up a north pole on the surface of the armature. The attraction of these unlike poles leads to a torque on the armature in the negative direction, corresponding to generator action if $v$ is positive. Hence, with the convention of page 12, the associated component of electrical input power must be negative, so that the rotation voltage term $(-M_f\nu i_f)$ has the negative sign. The term $(-M_d\nu i_d)$ also has a negative sign, because positive currents $i_d$ and $i_f$ produce fields in the same direction.

A similar argument shows that the rotation voltages in the direct-axis armature circuit due to quadrature-axis currents have a positive sign.

In Sect. 10 the derivation of the equations of a D.C. machine is discussed more fully. In Chap. VI it is shown that the equations of an A.C. machine can be expressed in the same form as those of a D.C. machine, if the variables are the fictitious axis voltages and currents determined by Park's transformation, instead of the actual quantities. Thus the equations for the generalised machine and the methods of solution discussed in this chapter apply equally to A.C. or D.C. machines.

The four equations given by Eqns. (2.3) refer to a machine represented by the four coils of Fig. 5. In general, a machine represented in the diagram by $n$ coils has $n$ voltage equations, relating $n$ voltages to $n$ currents. The impedance matrix of such a machine has $n^2$ compartments.

## *The general torque equation*

At any instant the torque developed by the machine depends on the currents flowing in the windings. An equation for the torque can be deduced from the voltage equations by considering the instantaneous power.

The torque developed by the interaction between the flux and the currents is called the *electrical torque,* and differs from the externally applied torque, if the speed varies, because of the inertia of the machine.

Let $f_e$ be the instantaneous electrical torque, defined as positive when mechanical power is passing into the machine from outside at a positive speed;

$f_t$ be the instantaneous applied torque (any friction or mechanical damping torque is assumed to be included with $f_t$);

$J$ be the moment of inertia.

31

Then:
$$f_t = f_e + J\frac{dv}{dt}. \qquad \qquad ...(2.4)$$

The convention adopted is intended to bring out the analogy between the electrical and mechanical quantities. Voltage is applied to the terminals and torque is applied to the shaft. Hence, apart from the effect of losses, positive voltage and current mean motoring action, and positive torque and speed mean generating action.

### Mechanical units in the per-unit system

The total power $P$ supplied to a machine electrically is the sum of the powers supplied to the individual circuits. (The capital letter $P$ is used for the instantaneous power in order to avoid confusion with the operator $p$.) In the per-unit system it is desirable that the power input should have a value equal or close to unity when the voltages and currents in the main circuits have unit values. For machines having several main circuits it is therefore necessary to introduce a factor $k_p$ in the formula for power and to choose the value of $k_p$ according to the particular type of machine. Then

$$P = k_p \Sigma ei. \qquad \qquad ...(2.5)$$

The *unit of power* is defined as the power corresponding to unit voltage and unit current in all the main circuits. For example, for a three-phase machine, unit power is that supplied when unit R.M.S. current flows at unit R.M.S. voltage and at unity power factor in all three phases. Hence for a three-phase machine the value of $k_p$ is $\frac{1}{3}$. For a cross-field generator, in which only one of the armature circuits is a main circuit, the unit of power is the power given by rated current at rated voltage in this circuit, and hence $k_p = 1$. In general $k_p$ is the reciprocal of the number of main circuits.

It may be noted that, with the above definition, unit power in an A.C. machine is not the actual rated power, but the power corresponding to rated kVA. Thus for an alternator having a rating of 1000 kVA. at 0·8 power factor, unit power equals 1000 kW. The rated power is 800 kW., or 0·8 per-unit.

The *unit of speed* adopted here is the radian per second. Any machine has a *nominal speed*, denoted by $\omega$, which can be used as a basis of reference. In a D.C. machine the nominal speed is the normal rated speed of the equivalent two-pole machine in 'electrical' radians per second. In an A.C. machine the nominal speed is the synchronous speed of the equivalent two-pole machine, and thus equals $2\pi$ times the supply frequency.

The *unit of torque*, in the per-unit system, is defined as the torque which produces unit power at the nominal speed $\omega$.

The moment of inertia of the machine, in the per-unit system, is expressed by the *inertia constant*, denoted by $H$, and defined by the following formula:

$$H = \frac{\text{Stored energy at synchronous speed in kW. secs.}}{\text{Rated kVA.}}.$$

The inertia constant, which is usually calculated from the moment of inertia and the speed in normal units, has the dimensions of time and its value is given in seconds. In the per-unit system the *unit of energy* is given by unit power acting for one second, and hence $H$ is numerically equal to the per-unit stored energy. If the machine were accelerated uniformly from rest to the nominal speed $\omega$ in one second, the torque would be, from Eqn. (2.4), equal to $J\omega$. The stored energy is that produced by the power corresponding to this torque at the mean speed $\dfrac{\omega}{2}$, and therefore, with the above definition of unit torque, equals $\frac{1}{2}J\omega$. Hence

$$H = \tfrac{1}{2}J\omega$$

or

$$J = \frac{2H}{\omega},$$

and Eqn. (2.4) becomes

$$f_t = f_e + \frac{2H}{\omega}pv. \qquad \qquad \ldots(2.6)$$

The per-unit system has the advantage, as mentioned on page 19, that the quantities for different machines are of the same order of magnitude. The inertia constant, which is used mainly for synchronous machines, has a value from two to six seconds for a wide range of designs of different sizes and speeds.

The per-unit system, as applied to the mechanical quantities, has the disadvantage that the dimensional consistency of the equations is lost.

## Calculation of electrical torque

Considering only the rotor coil $D$ of Fig. 5, the power $P_d$ supplied to this coil is, from Eqn. (2.3):

$$P_d = k_p e_d i_d$$

$$= k_p \left[ r_d i_d{}^2 + L_d i_d \frac{di_d}{dt} + M_{df} i_d \frac{di_f}{dt} + M_q v i_d i_q + M_g v i_d i_g \right].$$

In the above expression for $P_d$, the first term is the ohmic loss, and the second and third terms give the rate of change of stored magnetic energy in the machine. Only the fourth and fifth terms contribute to the output power corresponding to the electrical torque. It therefore follows that the total power $P_e$, corresponding to the torque developed by the interaction between flux and current, is determined by adding together the terms obtained by multiplying all the rotation voltages by the corresponding currents. Hence for the machine represented in Fig. 5:

$$P_e = k_p v (M_q i_d i_q + M_g i_d i_g - M_f i_q i_f - M_d i_d i_q). \qquad \ldots(2.7)$$

Using the definition of electrical torque given on page 31, and the definition of unit torque on page 33:

$$P_e = -\frac{v}{\omega} f_e.$$

The negative sign appears because $P_e$ is derived from the electrical power passing into the terminals, whereas $f_e$ is defined as a torque applied to the shaft. The following expression is therefore obtained for the electrical torque:

$$f_e = \omega k_p [M_f i_q i_f - M_g i_d i_g + (M_d - M_q) i_d i_q]. \qquad \ldots(2.8)$$

Eqn. (2.8) applies particularly to a machine represented by the four coils in Fig. 5, for which the equations are those stated in Eqns. (2.3). In the more general case the same method can be used, although there may be more or fewer terms depending on the number of rotation voltage terms in the equations and the expression for $f_e$ can be written down for any machine in the same way. If then the value of $f_e$ is substituted in Eqn. (2.6), an equation is obtained giving $f_t$ in terms of the currents and the speed.

### 6. Types of Problem and Methods of Solution

For a machine represented in the idealised diagram by $n$ coils, there are thus $n$ voltage equations and one torque equation; for example, $n=4$ for Fig. 5 and Eqns. (2.3) and (2.8). The time $t$ is the independent variable while the dependent variables are the $n$ currents and the speed. If the $n$ applied voltages and the applied torque are known, these $(n+1)$ equations are sufficient to determine the $n$ currents and the speed. Hence theoretically the performance of the machine is completely determined.

In the general case, the equations which contain product terms involving the speed and the currents are non-linear differential equations and are difficult to solve. For particular conditions, however, considerable simplifications can often be made, and the types of problem encountered in practice can be classified in the manner described in the following paragraphs and tabulated in Table 1. Some of the mathematical methods mentioned in Table 1 are discussed in Sects. 7, 8 and 9.

Under steady conditions the speed is constant and the voltage equations can be dealt with independently of the torque equations. The voltage equations, as mentioned on page 27, reduce under steady conditions to a set of $n$ ordinary linear algebraic equations, containing real variables for D.C. conditions (Item 1), or complex variables for A.C. conditions (Item 2).

Under transient conditions, when voltages and currents may vary in any manner, the problem is greatly simplified if the speed has a known constant value (Item 3), because the voltage equations, which can then still be handled independently of the torque equation, are linear equations with constant coefficients.

When the voltages are known the equations can be solved, either by algebraic methods for steady-state problems, or by operational methods for transient problems, and the currents thus obtained can be substituted in the torque equation. If the

35

speed is constant the externally applied torque is obtained directly because it is equal to the electrical torque.

A more difficult type of problem, under Item 3, is met in the study of the unbalanced operation of a polyphase machine, when the applied voltages $e_d$ and $e_q$ are not known explicitly, but are determined by known relations. Algebraic and operational methods may still be used, but become more laborious (see Sect. 41).

TABLE 1

| Condition | Equation | Method of Solution | Solution |
|---|---|---|---|
| SPEED CONSTANT. VOLTAGE EQUATIONS ONLY | | | |
| 1. Steady D.C. | Real algebraic equations | Real algebra | Real numbers |
| 2. Steady A.C. | Complex algebraic equations | Complex algebra Vector diagram Network analyser | Complex numbers |
| 3. Transient | Linear D.E's Constant coefficients | Operational methods | Functions of $t$ |
| SPEED A KNOWN FUNCTION OF $t$. VOLTAGE EQUATIONS ONLY | | | |
| 4. Transient | Linear D.E's Variable coefficients | Step-by-step calcn. Differential analyser Computer | Functions of $t$ |
| SPEED UNKNOWN. VOLTAGE AND TORQUE EQUATIONS | | | |
| 5. Transient | Non-linear D.E.'s | As 4 | Functions of $t$ |
| 6. Small changes | Linear D.E.'s Constant coefficients | As 3 | Functions of $t$ |
| 7. Small oscillations | Complex algebraic equations | As 2 | Complex numbers |

The next stage in difficulty arises if the speed varies but is a known function of time (Item 4). It is then still possible to solve the voltage equations separately, but the coefficients, which depend on the speed, are not constant. The equations are linear equations with variable coefficients for which the operational method does not apply. Usually only numerical solutions are possible, either by direct computation or with the aid of a computing device. Once the currents are determined the electrical torque is found by substitution in Eqn. (2.8). If the applied torque is required, the inertia term in Eqn. (2.6) must be added.

The most difficult problems are those for which the speed is an unknown variable (Item 5). This condition covers the most general type of transient problem, for which all the $(n+1)$ equations must be handled together by a numerical method.

The rather special conditions covered by Items 6 and 7 can be treated in a much simpler manner than the general case. For a small variation relative to a given steady condition, the non-linear differential equations, including both voltage and torque equations, can, to a close approximation, be converted into linear ones. When the variations take the form of sinusoidal oscillations at a known frequency, they can be further reduced to complex algebraic equations. The method of deriving the equations for small changes or small oscillations is explained in detail in Sect. 12.

## Applications of the theory

In developing the generalised theory of all types of electrical machine, the method here adopted is, first of all, to consider each of the main types separately, but to do it in such a way that the analysis of each type follows a common line. As already explained, the common line is to derive general differential equations for each machine based on a resolution of the windings along two axes at right angles.

Historically, starting with Faraday's experiments, the machine which comes first is the alternator, and there are many reasons why this could be considered to be the fundamental electrical machine. Indeed the general equations of the synchronous machine, first derived by Park in 1929, contain most of the fundamental ideas underlying the general theory of all machines.

As already mentioned, however, the most important idea in Park's work is the *transformation* made to replace the voltages and currents in rotating windings by equivalent axis quantities. Coupled with this in the general theory is the concept, introduced by Kron, of fictitious *axis coils* having the special pseudo-stationary property defined on page 15. This property, which is possessed by the actual circuits of a D.C. armature, serves as a link between the different types of machine, and makes it convenient, in a treatment such as the present one, to start with the D.C. type of machine, which has two obvious axes on both stator and rotor. The axes on the stator are fixed by the salient poles, and the axes on the rotor are fixed by the brushes. Hence the D.C. machine must necessarily be analysed by means of a two-axis theory, and in fact the commutator winding serves to explain at the outset the nature of the special pseudo-stationary property of the rotor windings of the generalised machine. The general theory of the D.C. machine applies also to many types of single-phase A.C. commutator machine (see page 214).

After the discussion of the D.C. machine in Chaps. III and IV, the synchronous machine and the induction motor are treated at considerable length in Chaps. V to X, which deal with many important practical problems. The synchronous machine has two obvious axes on the field element, whether it is of the salient-pole type or the cylindrical-rotor type, and consequently, although for the latter type it is possible to study certain limited problems without bringing in the two axes, any comprehensive analysis is bound to introduce them. On the other hand, the asynchronous machines (induction motor or polyphase commutator machine) have no definite axes on either element, and, when operating under balanced polyphase conditions, lend themselves to analysis by means of rotating fields. Even with these machines, however, a comprehensive theory must be based on the two-axis approach. The two-axis theory, or 'cross-field theory', of the induction motor is preferable for unbalanced A.C. conditions, and for transient conditions it is almost essential. The formal treatment of polyphase commutator machines follows the same lines as that of the induction motor, but is more complicated because of the additional windings.

Chap. XI explains briefly how the generalised theory can be used as the starting-point for the analysis of any type of machine. The application of the theory to any particular type depends on the transformation used to change from the variables in the generalised equations to those of the actual machine.

## 7. Representation of Sinusoidal Quantities by Harmonic Vectors and Complex Numbers

A geometrical vector is defined as a straight line having direction as well as magnitude. The use of vectors to represent alternating quantities was first introduced as a geometrical process, in which the instantaneous value of a quantity was given by the projection on a fixed line of a vector rotating at constant speed. Since the vectors representing quantities of a given frequency all rotate at the same speed, their relative angular positions, representing phase differences, can be shown on a stationary vector diagram. The steady-state theories of A.C. machines, particularly those in the earlier textbooks, are usually worked out in terms of vector diagrams of this type. In order to distinguish lag from lead in relation to any pair of harmonic quantities represented in a stationary vector diagram, it is necessary to have a convention as to which way the diagram has to be rotated in order that the projections of its component vectors shall give the instantaneous values of the quantities represented. In Britain the normal direction is counter-clockwise.

It was later recognised that the *harmonic vectors* in the stationary diagram could be expressed by complex numbers, which provide a valuable aid to rapid calculation. The real and imaginary parts of the complex number give the components of the vector along two fixed axes at right angles. The vector is thus defined by the co-ordinates of a point in an 'Argand diagram', on which the two parts of the complex number are plotted. When a complex number is used to represent an alternating voltage or current in this way, it is important to remember that it applies to a stationary vector and not to a rotating one.

The voltage vector diagram of a circuit expresses the fact that all the voltages add up to zero at every instant by representing them as geometrical vectors forming a closed polygon. The fact can equally well be expressed by an equation, called a *vector equation*, in which the sum of all the complex numbers representing the voltages is equal to zero, and it will be shown in this section how the general differential equations of a machine can be converted into vector equations if it is known that all the variables in the equations alternate at the same frequency; that is, if the machine operates under steady A.C. conditions.

The vector and the complex number represent the same quantity, and although the two terms have rather different meanings depending on the line of approach, they are to some extent interchangeable. In the analytical treatment followed here, the complex number is more prominent, while the geometrical vector is merely a useful device for giving a visual representation. Nevertheless, for convenience, a complex number may sometimes be referred to as a 'vector', as in the term 'vector equation' just defined.

It should be noted that a harmonic vector is not necessarily a 'time vector'; that is, a vector representing a quantity varying sinusoidally with time. Harmonic vectors may also represent quantities distributed sinusoidally in space. Such 'space vectors' are important in the theory of electrical machines (see page 86).

Since, as previously emphasised, a vector or complex number representing an alternating quantity is different in kind from the quantity itself, the symbols used for vectors or complex numbers should be clearly distinguished from those used for instantaneous values. The former are hereafter denoted by capital letters in heavy type (except in a few instances where Greek symbols are used), while instantaneous values are denoted by small letters. For example, an instantaneous current is denoted by $i$, and the complex number representing it by $\mathbf{I}$.

### Geometrical derivation

The geometrical relation between a rotating vector representing an alternating quantity and the instantaneous value of the quantity is that the latter may be measured by the projection of the vector on a fixed reference line. In Fig. 8 the projection on $OX$ of the rotating vector $OP$ is the instantaneous current $i$. The line $OA$ is a reference vector rotating at constant speed $\omega$. $OP$ makes a constant angle $\varphi$ with $OA$, and its magnitude is $I_m$.

### Analytical derivation

An alternating current is fully expressed in the following equation:

$$i = I_m \cos (\omega t + \varphi),$$

**40**

where $I_m=$ the maximum value of the current,

$\varphi=$ the phase angle of the current,

$\omega=2\pi$ times the frequency.

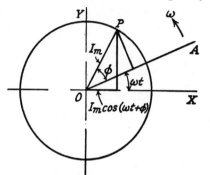

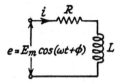

FIG. 8.—Diagram illustrating the derivation of a harmonic vector.

FIG. 9.—Diagram of a simple A.C. circuit.

Now $\cos(\omega t+\varphi)$ may be expressed as the real part of $\varepsilon^{j(\omega t+\varphi)}$, written $Re\{\varepsilon^{j(\omega t+\varphi)}\}$, and hence

$$i=Re\left\{\sqrt{2}\left(\frac{I_m}{\sqrt{2}}\varepsilon^{j\varphi}\right)\varepsilon^{j\omega t}\right\},$$

$$i=Re\{\sqrt{2}\mathbf{I}\varepsilon^{j\omega t}\}, \qquad\qquad \text{...(2.9)}$$

where $\mathbf{I}=\dfrac{I_m}{\sqrt{2}}\varepsilon^{j\varphi}$.

Eqn. (2.9) gives the relation between the instantaneous current $i$ and the complex number $\mathbf{I}$ corresponding to a stationary vector in a vector diagram.

The complex number $\mathbf{I}$ defines the current completely. Its modulus $I_m/\sqrt{2}$ is the R.M.S. value of the current, and the phase angle $\varphi$ gives the time phase of the current. If $\mathbf{I}$ is known, the instantaneous value is readily found by Eqn. (2.9).

The application of complex numbers to the solution, for steady A.C. conditions, of the differential equations of a circuit or machine can be illustrated by a simple example. The differential equation of the simple inductive circuit shown in Fig. 9 is:

$$Ri+L\frac{di}{dt}=e, \qquad\qquad \text{...(2.10)}$$

where $e=E_m\cos(\omega t+\varphi)$.

41

The applied voltage $e$ can be represented by a complex number $\mathbf{E}$, where $\mathbf{E} = \dfrac{1}{\sqrt{2}} E_m \varepsilon^{j\varphi}$.

Let the current be represented by a complex number $\mathbf{I}$, as in Eqn. (2.9). Eqn. (2.10) can then be written:

$$\left(R + L\frac{d}{dt}\right)\left[Re\{\sqrt{2}\mathbf{I}\varepsilon^{j\omega t}\}\right] = Re\{\sqrt{2}\mathbf{E}\varepsilon^{j\omega t}\}.$$

Now

$$\frac{d}{dt} Re\{\varepsilon^{j(\omega t + \varphi)}\} = -\omega \sin(\omega t + \varphi) = Re\{j\omega\varepsilon^{j(\omega t + \varphi)}\},$$

and hence

$$Re\{(R + j\omega L)\mathbf{I}\varepsilon^{j\omega t}\} = Re\{\mathbf{E}\varepsilon^{j\omega t}\}.$$

This equation holds for all values of $t$, and hence

$$(R + j\omega L)\mathbf{I} = \mathbf{E}. \qquad \ldots(2.11)$$

Eqn. (2.11) is a vector equation, relating the two complex numbers $\mathbf{I}$ and $\mathbf{E}$. It may be compared with the original differential equation (2.10), which in operational form, with $p$ for $\dfrac{d}{dt}$, would be:

$$(R + Lp)i = e. \qquad \ldots(2.12)$$

The method by which the vector equation (2.11) has been derived holds for any set of linear differential equations with constant coefficients. It is evident that the terms of any differential equation of this type can be converted into complex numbers in the same way, and consequently that the complete equation can be converted into a vector equation by the following two simple rules:

1. Change the symbols for all variables by replacing the small letters (instantaneous values) by heavy capital letters (complex numbers).

2. Replace $p$ by $j\omega$.

It should be emphasised that the vector method, like the principle of superposition and the operational methods explained in Sect. 8, only applies if the differential equations are linear and have constant coefficients. A circuit governed by a non-linear differential equation, or one having non-linear elements, cannot have a solution in which all the voltages and currents are sinusoidal. This point brings out again the importance of the initial assumption that there is no saturation.

### Power in A.C. circuits

In a circuit with alternating voltage and current of a given frequency, the power does not alternate at the same frequency. Its value is made up of a constant part, known as the *mean power*, and a part alternating at double frequency. The expression for the instantaneous power can be obtained by determining the instantaneous values of voltage and current and multiplying them together. Often, however, all that is required is the mean power, and for this a simple formula is available.

Suppose that the instantaneous values are:

$$e = E_m \cos(\omega t + \varphi),$$
$$i = I_m \cos(\omega t + \varphi + \theta).$$

The mean power is

$$P = \tfrac{1}{2} E_m I_m \cos \theta. \qquad \ldots(2.13)$$

Expressed as complex numbers, the voltage and current vectors are:

$$\mathbf{E} = \frac{1}{\sqrt{2}} E_m \varepsilon^{j\varphi},$$

$$\mathbf{I} = \frac{1}{\sqrt{2}} I_m \varepsilon^{j(\varphi + \theta)}.$$

The expression for $P$ in Eqn. (2.13) can be written:

$$P = \tfrac{1}{2} E_m I_m \,.\, Re\{\varepsilon^{j\theta}\}$$
$$= Re\left\{ \frac{1}{\sqrt{2}} E_m \varepsilon^{-j\varphi} \,.\, \frac{1}{\sqrt{2}} I_m \varepsilon^{j(\varphi + \theta)} \right\}$$
$$= Re\{\mathbf{E}^* \mathbf{I}\}, \qquad \ldots(2.14)$$

or alternatively

$$P = Re\{\mathbf{E}\,\mathbf{I}^*\}, \qquad \ldots(2.15)$$

where $\mathbf{E}^*$ and $\mathbf{I}^*$ are the *complex conjugates* of $\mathbf{E}$ and $\mathbf{I}$. The complex conjugate of a complex number is defined as the number obtained by reversing the sign of the imaginary part; that is, the conjugate of $(a+jb)$ is $(a-jb)$.

These formulae provide the most convenient means of calculating the mean power when the voltages and currents are represented by complex numbers.

## 8. The Heaviside Operational Method

The methods of the operational calculus are of great assistance in handling the differential equations arising in the analysis of electrical machines. They are valuable for stating the equations in an abbreviated form, for manipulating them, and, in certain types of problem, for obtaining the solution.

It was explained in connection with Table 1, page 36, that, when the speed of the machine is constant (Item 3), or if small changes of the variables, including the speed, are considered (Item 6), the differential equations are linear and have constant coefficients. For a set of simultaneous equations of this kind the operational calculus provides a simple method of solution if the initial conditions are known. If, however, the speed of the machine is not constant, the coefficients are variable (Item 4), or some of the equations are non-linear (Item 5), and the simple operational methods do not apply.

The Heaviside operational method (Ref. 44.1), introduced by Heaviside in the early days of circuit analysis, replaces $\frac{d}{dt}$ by $p$ in the equations, and then treats the operator $p$ as an algebraic quantity. The solution of a set of linear equations is obtained by manipulating the equations algebraically in accordance with certain definite rules, based on comparison with known solutions. Heaviside did not provide a rigorous mathematical basis for the method, but mathematicians have since established satisfactory proofs. The use of the Heaviside method for obtaining a solution is limited here to the simpler problems of the kind considered in the following pages. Care is needed in its application to ensure that the necessary conditions are complied with.

*Solution of linear problems*

The application of the Heaviside method to problems involving linear differential equations with constant coefficients

44

is explained in the following pages in relation to a simple example. The method applies directly to conditions where the variables in the equations are initially zero, as in the problem discussed below. It is explained later how the method can be extended, by using the principle of superposition, to short-circuit problems of the type discussed in Sects. 13 and 32.

The problem of the example is to determine the primary current of the transformer of Fig. 6, when its secondary circuit is closed and the primary winding is switched on to a constant

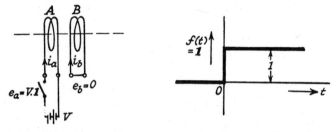

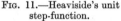

FIG. 10.—Transformer with a      FIG. 11.—Heaviside's unit
suddenly applied D.C. voltage.          step-function.

voltage $V$, as indicated in Fig. 10. The secondary resistance and inductance may if necessary include the constants of an external impedance.

If zero time is chosen to be the instant at which the switch is closed, the applied voltage $e_a$ is zero when $t<0$, and has the constant value $V$ when $t>0$; $e_a$ is thus a *step-function voltage*, and equals $V\mathbf{1}$, where $\mathbf{1}$ is the Heaviside *unit step-function*, represented in Fig. 11. Eqns. (1.4) with $e_a=V\mathbf{1}$ and $e_b=0$, become:

$$(r_a+L_ap)i_a+M_{ab}pi_b=V\mathbf{1} \left.\right\}$$
$$M_{ab}pi_a+(r_b+L_bp)i_b=0 \quad\quad \quad \dots(2.16)$$

The Heaviside operational method treats the operator $p$ as an algebraic quantity in order to obtain the currents as explicit functions of $p$. The operational expression for $i_a$, obtained by eliminating $i_b$ algebraically, is then:

$$i_a=\frac{(r_b+L_bp)}{(r_a+L_ap)(r_b+L_bp)-M_{ab}{}^2p^2} \cdot V\mathbf{1}. \quad\dots(2.17)$$

In machine and circuit problems it is usually convenient to express the characteristics as far as possible in terms of time constants rather than in terms of the separate resistances and inductances, because, apart from the fact that the expressions become less cumbersome, the solutions contain exponential factors in which the rate of decrement is given by a time constant. In the present example there are two time constants, primary and secondary.

$$T_a = \frac{L_a}{r_a},$$

$$T_b = \frac{L_b}{r_b}.$$

Equation (2.17) then becomes:

$$i_a = \frac{1 + T_b p}{(1 + T_a p)(1 + T_b p) - \dfrac{M_{ab}^2 p^2}{r_a r_b}} \cdot \frac{V}{r_a} \mathbf{1}. \qquad \ldots(2.18)$$

*Solution by the Heaviside method*

To evaluate $i_a$ as a function of time the expression in (2.18) must be split up into partial fractions, which can then be evaluated separately. For the present problem it is first necessary to factorise the denominator of the right-hand side of Eqn. (2.18) by writing it in the form:

$$i_a = \frac{1 + T_b p}{(1 + T_a' p)(1 + T_b' p)} \cdot \frac{V}{r_a} \mathbf{1}, \qquad \ldots(2.19)$$

where $T_a'$ and $T_b'$ are new time constants, the values of which are found by solving the quadratic equation obtained by equating the denominator to zero.

The most convenient form of partial fractions for this example is obtained from the identity:

$$\frac{1 + T_b p}{(1 + T_a' p)(1 + T_b' p)} = 1 - \frac{A T_a' p}{1 + T_a' p} - \frac{B T_b' p}{1 + T_b' p}, \qquad \ldots(2.20)$$

where $A$ and $B$ are constants.

The constant $A$ can best be determined by multiplying both

sides of Eqn. (2.20) by $(1+T_a'p)$ and then putting $p=-1/T_a'$, whence

$$A=\frac{(T_a'-T_b)}{(T_a'-T_b')}.$$

Similarly

$$B=\frac{(T_b'-T_b)}{(T_b'-T_a')}.$$

The application of the Heaviside method depends on the following rule:

$$\frac{p}{p+a}\mathbf{1}=\varepsilon^{-at} \qquad \qquad \dots(2.21)$$

or alternatively

$$\frac{Tp}{Tp+1}\mathbf{1}=\varepsilon^{-t/T}, \qquad \qquad \dots(2.22)$$

where $a$ and $T$ are constants $(T=1/a)$.

The solution of the transformer problem is therefore:

$$i_a=\left[1-\frac{AT_a'p}{1+T_a'p}-\frac{BT_b'p}{1+T_b'p}\right]\frac{V}{r_a}\mathbf{1}$$

$$=(1-A\varepsilon^{-t/T_a'}-B\varepsilon^{-t/T_b'})\frac{V}{r_a}. \qquad \dots(2.23)$$

*Higher order equations*

In more complicated problems there may be more equations and more variables. However, provided that the differential equations are linear and have constant coefficients, the operational expression for any variable, obtained by algebraic elimination of the other variables, is always of the type:

$$i=\frac{g(p)}{f(p)}\mathbf{1}, \qquad \qquad \dots(2.24)$$

where $g(p)$ and $f(p)$ are polynomial expressions in $p$. The typical form of the function $f(p)$ is:

$$f(p)=a_np^n+a_{n-1}p^{n-1}+ \dots +a_1p+a_0,$$

where $n$ (an integer) is the order of the polynomial,
$a_0, a_1, \dots a_{n-1}, a_n$ are constants.

The function $g(p)$ is a similar polynomial expression of order not greater than $n$.

By obtaining the roots of the equation $f(p)=0$, the denominator of Eqn. (2.24) may be factorised, and Eqn. (2.24) expressed in partial fraction form.

$$i=\left[A_0+\sum_{n=1}^{n}\frac{A_n p}{p+a_n}\right]1, \qquad \ldots(2.25)$$

where $A_0$, $A_1$, $A_2$, ... $A_n$ are constants,

$a_0$, $a_1$, $a_2$, ... $a_n$ are the negatives of the $n$ roots of $f(p)=0$, assumed to be all different.

The solution is then

$$i=A_0+\sum_{n=1}^{n}A_n\varepsilon^{-a_n t}. \qquad \ldots(2.26)$$

## 9. Analysers and Computers for Electrical Machine Problems

As already mentioned, the application to practical problems of the theories given in this book often requires lengthy numerical calculations. In the past the design calculations for electrical machines have for the most part been carried out with a slide rule and often consumed a great deal of time. Many types of computer have, however, now been developed and can be used with advantage for this kind of work. The benefit obtained is much more than a direct saving of time, because it becomes possible to do additional computational work which otherwise cannot be undertaken at all. Many existing methods have had to be simplified to the point where the results are of doubtful value because a more exact treatment would require an excessive amount of manual computation. The A.C. network analyser is a good example of a computer which at first met with opposition from those who claimed that existing methods were sufficient, but which now has many uses outside the range of its original field of application.

The computers available for obtaining the numerical solution of any of the problems considered can be classified under two main headings as follows:

An *analogue computer* is built up from elements which represent the system in such a way that the quantities to be determined can be measured on the computer. An element of the analogue computer may be of the same type as the system component to which it corresponds, thus serving to some extent as a *model*, or it may differ in kind, functioning more obviously as an *analogue*.

A *digital computer* consists of elements which perform the arithmetical operations required for solving the equations of the system. Any mathematical operation can be carried out as a succession of additions or subtractions performed on the digits of the numbers used in the calculation.

The inherent accuracy of a digital computer depends only on the number of digits available for the various stages of its operations, while that of an analogue computer depends on the accuracy with which its components represent the elements of the actual apparatus and upon the accuracy of the equipment with which the measurements are made. In general, although digital computers are inherently more accurate than analogue computers, the latter can be designed to give results within normal engineering tolerances. Moreover it is easier on the analogue type of computer to make changes in the parameters of the system and to observe the effect of making such changes.

The field of application of computers covers the whole range of scientific work for which numerical calculations have to be made. For problems relating to electrical machines, particularly when they form part of a composite system, the computing devices used in the past have been mainly of the analogue type and are generally known as *analysers*. There are, however, many possible applications of the digital computer to such problems.

*Types of analogue computer*

The most obvious type of computing device is an exact small-scale model on the lines of a hydraulic model, but such exact representation is rarely possible for composite electrical systems. An element of an analogue computer is frequently a model of a system component in the sense that it is of the same type, although differing greatly in shape; for example, a small iron-cored reactor may represent the reactance of a transmission line. In other analogue computers the elements are of a different type from the system components and correspond to them by analogy. The term 'analogue computer' is used for all these devices because even those that are most nearly models operate to some extent by analogy.

When there is a close correspondence between the elements of the analyser and the actual system, the analyser can be set up directly from the diagram of the system without reference to the equations. In other types of analogue computer, in which the analogy is less direct, it is necessary to formulate the equations before the computer can be used. The former type has the advantage that it provides a direct representation of the operation of the system, and saves time in carrying out the computation. For a full understanding of the manner of application of the analyser, however, the equations are still very important, because they express the fundamental relationships in the most general way.

The most realistic method of representing an electrical system is to build up a network of model machines, impedances and other apparatus, connected so as to correspond with the equipment forming the actual system. An analyser of this type used for power-system problems is called a *micro-system* (Ref. 50.1). The generators, synchronous condensers and motors, which are called *micro-machines*, represent closely the characteristics of the machines in the actual system, although they differ greatly from them in physical proportions. Such miniature machines can represent both steady and transient characteristics and can introduce non-linear effects. Similarly a model control system can be built up from direct-current micro-machines in conjunction with amplifiers and other devices, or a model network can be made with impedances only.

Some types of analyser are suitable primarily for the study of steady-state problems. The *resistance network analyser* was the earliest type; the original ones used direct current and were called 'D.C. calculating boards', but alternating current is now sometimes used. A more complete analysis of an A.C. system can be made with an *A.C. network analyser*, which is a small-scale network containing elements with both resistance and reactance. Network analysers of this type, which are used extensively for the study of power-system problems, operate with only a single phase and provide a less exact representation of the generator than the micro-systems described above. They normally operate at a single frequency and their application is limited to problems for which the system can be replaced by an equivalent network (Ref. 45.3).

An alternative method of dealing with steady A.C. problems is provided by the *transformer analogue analyser*. In this type of analyser the elements consist of variable-ratio transformers, which are used to multiply real or complex numbers. It is suitable for a wider range of problems than the A.C. network analyser, because it can solve problems for which the system cannot be represented by an equivalent network (Ref. 53.2).

Transient problems can be investigated by means of a model network, sometimes called a *transient analyser*, or by a micro-system, as already mentioned. Alternatively an equipment based on analogue representation can be used. A *differential analyser* is a device of this kind, which can be set up from the equations of the system so that the quantities in the analogue obey the same differential equations as the corresponding quantities in the system. Two principal types have been developed. In the mechanical differential analyser the variables are represented by the motion of shafts, while in the electronic type they are represented by voltages and currents. Both types include elements of different kinds for adding, multiplying, integrating, and for deriving functions of the variables. A problem solved with the aid of a differential analyser is discussed on page 160 (Ref. 45.3).

*Types of digital computer*

Digital computers may be divided into three classes—manual, semi-automatic and automatic. *Manual computers* include the familiar manual desk computer, which is essentially an adding machine but can be used for multiplying or dividing by successive addition or subtraction. *Semi-automatic* computers include power-operated desk calculating machines as well as the punched-card machines extensively used for accounting purposes. Such computers are capable of performing several simple arithmetical operations, but require an operator to feed them

51

with figures and instructions at each stage of the computation. They normally work with the decimal system of digits.

*Automatic computers* have extensive internal facilities for the storage of data and operating instructions and can perform a complete computation without further action by an operator. In recent years a number of large automatic high-speed digital computers, using many electronic valves to perform difficult mathematical computations, have been built. The units are essentially adding devices, as in the manual and semi-automatic computers, but they almost always use the binary system of digits. A general discussion of digital computers is given in Ref. 53.1.

*Application of the computers*

Before a computing device can be used for the solution of a practical problem it is necessary to formulate the problem either in terms of mathematical equations or of an equivalent circuit or system, which can be transferred directly on to the analyser or computer. The result must then be interpreted and verified before it can be of practical value. Thus the analyser or computer only performs the mathematical part of the analysis. Such aids to computation can, however, be of immense value and should be used much more widely than they have been in the past for the solution of electrical machine problems (Ref. 54.3).

# CHAPTER III

## *The D.C. Machine*

### 10. The Equations of the D.C. Machine

The basic theory of the D.C. machine, expressed by its equations, is very simple because of the clear separation of the two axes. The practical application is more difficult because of the subsidiary effects that have to be neglected in the general linear theory; perhaps more so than in any other type of machine. The practical designer is most often concerned with such things as commutation, saturation and armature reaction, and it is these topics that fill the majority of textbooks on D.C. machines. Saturation has an extremely important effect on the operation of a D.C. machine. Without it the operation of a shunt-excited generator would not be possible. Also, because of saturation, the armature reaction due to the armature current affects the main flux. Sometimes these non-linear effects must be dealt with independently on their merits, while at other times they may be allowed for approximately within the framework of the linear theory. Examples of both these methods are given later.

In distinction, however, from the above subsidiary effects, the main principles of operation of D.C. machines may be dealt with in terms of the simple linear theory. Even for steady D.C. operation, when the voltages are simply the resistance drops and the E.M.F. induced in the rotor due to the rotation, a clearer picture is obtained by first considering an idealised machine and allowing for the subsidiary effects subsequently. For transient conditions, the equations based on a linear theory provide the only reasonable method of analysis, although saturation and commutation are still important and make some practical adjustment necessary. Again, the D.C. machine is an important element in modern control systems, and, for complicated equipments comprising several machines, a workable theory can only be obtained by idealising the components.

The voltage equations of the cross-field D.C. machine

represented in Fig. 4 were stated without a full proof in Eqns. (2.3). The result can be justified by considering each term separately as being the voltage which would arise in the circuit concerned if there were current in only one of the four circuits, the other three carrying no current. The terms for resistance drops or voltages induced in stator windings need no further explanation, but the armature voltages, already discussed on page 30, are considered in more detail in the following pages.

*Transformer voltages in the armature*

The transformer voltage induced between the brushes on either axis is proportional to the rate of change of the flux on

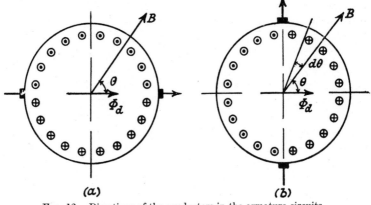

FIG. 12.—Directions of the conductors in the armature circuits.
(*a*) Direct axis.    (*b*) Quadrature axis.

that axis. The transformer voltage in the direct-axis armature circuit due to the main air-gap flux $\Phi_{md}$ may be written

$$e_{dt} = p\psi_{md}, \qquad \qquad ...(3.1)$$

where $\psi_{md}$ is the *flux linkage*, corresponding to $\Phi_{md}$, with the armature circuit. $\psi_{md}$ and $\Phi_{md}$ both depend on the curve of flux density in the air-gap. They are proportional to each other and the relation between them depends on the distribution both of the flux density and of the armature winding. The transformer voltages can thus be expressed by using inductance coefficients as in Eqns. (2.3).

If the distribution of the flux density is assumed to be sinusoidal, certain relations hold between the inductance coefficients which are of importance in connection with the generalised theory. The transformer voltage between the direct-axis brushes due to a direct-axis flux can be found by calculating the voltages induced in individual turns and integrating over half the circumference. In Fig. 12(a) the dots and crosses on the conductors indicate the directions in which armature conductors are traversed as the circuit is followed through in the positive direction between the direct-axis brushes. A positive current in this circuit would set up a flux along the positive direct axis in accordance with the convention stated on page 12.

If the direct-axis flux density curve is sinusoidal, with maximum value $B_m$, then

$$B = B_m \cos \theta,$$

and
$$\Phi_{md} = \int_{-\pi/2}^{\pi/2} Blrd\theta = 2B_m lr,$$

where $B$=air-gap flux density at the point $\theta$,
$\quad r$=radius of the armature,
$\quad l$=length of the armature core.

The flux linking a turn whose sides are located at the points $\theta$ and $(\pi + \theta)$ is:

$$\int_{(\pi+\theta)}^{\theta} B_m \cos \theta . lrd\theta = 2B_m lr \sin \theta$$
$$= \Phi_{md} \sin \theta.$$

The induced voltage in the turn is:

$$-\frac{d}{dt}(\Phi_{md} \sin \theta).$$

The transformer voltage between the direct-axis brushes, which is the negative of the induced voltage, is given by:

$$e_{dt} = \int_{0}^{\pi} \frac{d}{dt}(\Phi_{md} \sin \theta)z d\theta$$
$$= \frac{d}{dt}(2\Phi_{md}z).$$

where $z$=number of conductors per radian per layer.

Hence, from Eqn. (3.1), the flux linkage for a sinusoidal flux density wave is:

$$\psi_{md} = 2\Phi_{md}z.$$

Similarly, if the quadrature-axis flux distribution is sinusoidal, the transformer voltage is:

$$e_{qt} = p\psi_{mq}, \qquad \qquad \dots(3.2)$$

where $\psi_{mq} = 2\Phi_{mq}z$.

*Rotation voltages in the armature*

If currents flow in the direct-axis windings so as to set up a flux on the direct axis, the voltage induced between the quadrature-axis brushes due to the rotation can be found by calculating the voltages in the individual conductors and integrating over half the circumference. In Fig. 12(*b*) the dots and crosses on the conductors indicate the directions in which the armature conductors are traversed as the circuit is followed through in the positive direction between the quadrature-axis brushes.

The voltage in the positive direction in the conductors of both layers occupying a small part of the periphery subtending an angle $d\theta$ is, by the flux-cutting rule:

$$B.l.rv.2zd\theta.$$

The direct-axis flux is given by:

$$\Phi_{md} = \int_{-\pi/2}^{\pi/2} Blrd\theta.$$

The rotation voltage between the quadrature-axis brushes, which is the negative of the induced voltage, is therefore:

$$\begin{aligned} e_{qr} &= -\int_{-\pi/2}^{\pi/2} 2Blrvzd\theta \\ &= -2vz\Phi_{md} \\ &= -v\psi_{md}. \qquad \qquad \dots(3.3) \end{aligned}$$

Similarly the rotation voltage between the direct-axis brushes due to a quadrature-axis flux can be found in the same way.

The expression is of the same form as Eqn. (3.3), but now has a positive sign (see page 30):

$$e_{dr} = v\psi_{mq}. \qquad \qquad ...(3.4)$$

It should be noted that the result expressed by Eqns. (3.3) and (3.4) does not depend at all on the wave-form of the flux density curve. The field form curve of a D.C. machine does in practice depart considerably from a sinusoidal shape, but the generated voltage depends only on the area of the curve, which is proportional to the total flux per pole.

### Armature voltage equations

Eqns. (3.1) to (3.4) give the transformer and rotation voltages due to sinusoidal air-gap fluxes $\Phi_{md}$ and $\Phi_{mq}$ on the two axes, each flux being measured by the corresponding flux linkage $\psi_{md}$ or $\psi_{mq}$. In order to obtain the armature voltage equations the effect of the armature leakage must also be included. To do this it is assumed that the armature leakage flux acts in the same way as a sinusoidally distributed air-gap flux so far as both rotation and transformer voltages induced in the armature winding are concerned. Then, if $\psi_d$ and $\psi_q$ are the total direct-axis and quadrature-axis flux linkages with the armature, including leakage, the armature voltage equations are:

$$\left. \begin{array}{l} e_d = p\psi_d + v\psi_q + r_a i_d \\ e_q = -v\psi_d + p\psi_q + r_a i_q \end{array} \right\}, \qquad ...(3.5)$$

where $r_a$ is the armature resistance between a pair of brushes and is assumed to have the same value for either axis.

If the quantities are all measured in a per-unit system, the relations between the flux linkages and the currents in the windings on the same axis are given by the equations:

$$\left. \begin{array}{l} \psi_d = L_d i_d + M_{df} i_f \\ \psi_q = L_q i_q + M_{qg} i_g \end{array} \right\} \qquad ...(3.6)$$

where $L_d$, $L_q$, are the complete inductances of the armature circuits;

$M_{df}$, $M_{qg}$, are the mutual inductances between each armature circuit and the field winding on the same axis.

The voltage equations of the machine are thus:

$$
\begin{vmatrix} e_f \\ e_d \\ e_q \\ e_g \end{vmatrix} =
\begin{vmatrix}
r_f+L_f p & M_{df} p & & \\
M_{df} p & r_d+L_d p & L_q v & M_{qg} v \\
-M_{df} v & -L_d v & r_q+L_q p & M_{qg} p \\
& & M_{qg} p & r_g+L_g p
\end{vmatrix}
\cdot
\begin{vmatrix} i_f \\ i_d \\ i_q \\ i_g \end{vmatrix}
$$

$$...(3.7)$$

It must be emphasised again that these equations depend on the assumption that the flux linking the armature is sinusoidally distributed. They are of the same form as Eqns. (2.3) but, for the sinusoidal distribution, some of the coefficients in that equation are equal in pairs, viz.:

$$M_d = L_d, \quad M_f = M_{df},$$
$$M_q = L_q, \quad M_g = M_{qg}.$$

The presence of harmonics in the flux wave causes each pair to be no longer quite equal, although the values are still of the same order. For practical work on D.C. machines it is quite easy, if necessary, to derive the values of the more exact coefficients in Eqns. (2.3). Eqns. (3.7) give the equations of a generalised machine which, as shown in Chap. VI, apply to A.C. machines as well as D.C. machines.

*Application to a simple D.C. machine*

The simplest possible D.C. machine is illustrated by Fig. 13. (The stator winding shown dotted should be ignored for the present.) This machine has only two windings. The stator has a field winding $F$ on the pole axis (or direct axis) and the rotor has a commutator winding, with brushes located so that an armature current sets up a field on the quadrature axis. Hence the diagram represents a normal, separately excited D.C. machine with its brushes in the neutral position. As in Fig. 4, the armature circuit through the brushes in Fig. 13 can be replaced by an axis coil $Q$ on the quadrature axis. The coil $Q$ then has the pseudo-stationary property discussed on page 15.

The coils $F$ and $Q$ of Fig. 13 correspond to the coils $F$ and $Q$ in the generalised machine of Fig. 5, and the equations can be obtained from Eqns. (2.3) by omitting the second and fourth equations and the second and fourth columns of the impedance matrix. The equations of the machine of Fig. 13 are therefore:

$$\left.\begin{aligned} e_f &= (r_f + L_f p)i_f \\ e_q &= -M_f v i_f + (r_q + L_q p)i_q \end{aligned}\right\}. \qquad ...(3.8)$$

These two equations do not depend on any assumption that the flux wave is sinusoidal, since both the rotation voltage

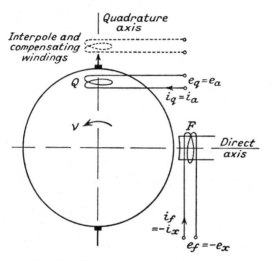

Fig. 13.—Diagram of a simple D.C. machine.

$-M_f v i_f$ in the armature winding and the voltage $L_f p i_f$ in the field winding depend on the total flux regardless of its distribution. $L_f$ and $L_q$ are the complete self-inductances of the windings. Eqns. (3.8) hold whether the quantities are expressed in ordinary units or are per-unit values.

For convenience in the application of these equations it is better to avoid the negative sign by introducing new symbols $e_x$ and $i_x$ for the exciting voltage and current, such that:

$$e_x = -e_f,$$
$$i_x = -i_f.$$

59

Also the suffix $a$ is used for the armature circuit instead of $q$. With these changes of notation, which are indicated on Fig. 13, the equations become:

$$\left.\begin{aligned} e_x &= (r_f + L_f p)i_x \\ e_a &= M_f v i_x + (r_a + L_a p)i_a \end{aligned}\right\} . \qquad \qquad \ldots(3.9)$$

The electrical torque is obtained from the rotation term by the method explained on page 34:

$$f_e = -k_t i_x i_a, \qquad \qquad \ldots(3.10)$$

where $k_t$ is a constant which depends on the units used. If $i_a$ and $i_x$ are positive, $f_e$ is negative and thus represents a motoring torque.

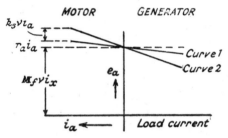

FIG. 14.—Characteristics of a D.C. machine.

The overall torque equation, obtained by combining Eqns. (2.4) and (3.10), is:

$$f_t = -k_t i_x i_a + J p v. \qquad \qquad \ldots(3.11)$$

For steady D.C. operation the currents do not vary with time, and hence the equations can be derived from Eqns. (3.9) by putting $p = 0$. They are:

$$\left.\begin{aligned} e_x &= r_f i_x \\ e_a &= M_f v i_x + r_a i_a \end{aligned}\right\} . \qquad \qquad \ldots(3.12)$$

The curve relating the voltage to the current of a D.C. generator, under steady conditions with a constant field current and constant speed, is shown in Fig. 14, Curve 1. With the sign convention adopted, $i_a$ is positive for a motor and negative for a generator. The positive value of $i_a$, corresponding to motoring operation, is plotted to the left in Fig. 14 in order to show the characteristic for a separately excited D.C. generator in the form usual in textbooks. For the idealised machine the curve is a straight line.

## 11. Interpole, Compensating and Series Windings

Additional windings on the D.C. machine can be allowed for by means of further coils on the idealised machine. For many practical purposes the analysis can be simplified by making approximations when determining what coils must be included.

### *Interpole and compensating windings*

Most modern D.C. machines have interpole windings, and some have compensating windings, connected in series with the armature. Both interpole and compensating windings, as indicated by the dotted coil in Fig. 13, set up M.M.F.s on the quadrature axis in direct opposition to the armature winding. For most purposes the combination of armature winding and interpole or compensating winding may be treated as a single winding, of which the resistance is the sum of the individual resistances while the combined inductance depends on how the windings are magnetically interlinked. Normally an interpole winding increases the effective value of armature inductance while a compensating winding reduces it. If revised values of resistance and inductance are used, Eqns. (3.9) and (3.10) still apply.

### *Series windings*

A series winding on the main poles, represented by the coil $S$ in Fig. 15, is frequently used in order to modify the steady-state characteristics of D.C. generators and motors. It is connected in series with the armature and the two windings $Q$ and $S$ form a single circuit indicated by the letter $A$. There are still only two equations but they contain extra terms:

$$\left.\begin{aligned} e_x &= (r_f + L_f p)i_x + Mpi_a \\ e_a &= M_f v i_x + k_s v i_a + (r_a + L_a p)i_a + Mpi_x \end{aligned}\right\}, \quad \ldots(3.13)$$

where $r_a$ = total resistance of circuit $A$,

$\quad L_a$ = total self-inductance of circuit $A$,

$\quad M$ = mutual inductance between coils $F$ and $S$,

$\quad k_s = NM_f$,

$\quad N$ = ratio of turns of coils $F$ and $S$.

The torque is obtained from the two rotation voltage terms, which are proportional to two components of flux on the direct axis. Hence

$$f_e = -k_t(i_x + Ni_a)i_a. \qquad \qquad ...(3.14)$$

The steady-state equations are:

$$\left.\begin{array}{l} e_x = r_f i_x \\ e_a = M_f v i_x + (r_a + k_s v)i_a \end{array}\right\}. \qquad ...(3.15)$$

For a machine with a *differential series winding*, in which the series ampere-turns oppose the field ampere-turns when the

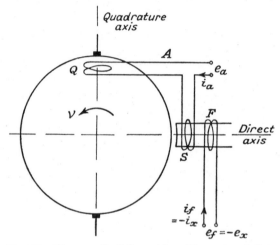

FIG. 15.—Diagram of a D.C. machine with a series winding.

machine is a generator ($i_a$ negative), $k_s$ is positive. Curve 2 of Fig. 14 shows the characteristic of such a machine, which has an increased droop on generator load. For a machine with a *cumulative series winding*, $k_s$ is negative and the effect on the characteristic is reversed. (Fig. 15 indicates the differential series connection, for which the generating current ($-i_a$) opposes the field current $i_x$.) Any desired slope, up or down, can thus be obtained by using an appropriate series winding. Practical curves differ from the idealised curves of Fig. 14 in having some curvature, but a straight line can be assumed as an approximation.

## Brush shift

If the brushes are not exactly in the neutral position, the armature current produces a component of flux on the direct axis. If the angular displacement is small, the effect is approximately equivalent to that of a series winding with appropriate values of $k_s$ and $M$, and Eqns. (3.13) to (3.15) apply. Brush displacement is often used in practice in order to obtain a fine adjustment of the characteristic, but there is bound to be a small error in any machine even when the brushes are intended to be in the neutral position.

Since the brush has a certain circumferential thickness the statement that the brushes are in the neutral position implies that the centre of the brush is on the axis and that the current is uniformly distributed over the brush. If the commutating conditions are not ideal, however, the effective centre of the brush differs from the actual centre. For example, for a machine without interpoles or with insufficient excitation on the interpoles, the effective brush position is displaced forwards from the mechanical neutral. Hence the characteristic of such a machine droops on the generator side because of this effective shift. The effect can be allowed for by using appropriate values of $k_s$ and $M$, as for a series winding. Since, however, the commutation effects are not exactly proportional to the current, the use of a constant value of $k_s$ is only an approximation.

## Armature reaction

In a machine with no saturation, the M.M.F. due to the armature current has no effect on the total flux in the poles. There is, however, a good deal of saturation in most D.C. machines, particularly when heavy currents flow, and as a result the main flux is reduced because of the cross magnetisation. The effect is not by any means proportional to the current and cannot strictly be taken into account in a linear theory. The effect on the steady-state characteristic of a separately excited generator is shown in Fig. 16. In this example the drop in the voltage between no-load and full-load is quite small, but if five times full-load current is made to flow through the generator, the demagnetisation due to armature reaction is so great that the terminal voltage is reduced to zero. Thus the armature reaction has the beneficial effect of limiting the short-circuit current of the generator.

The effect of armature reaction can be allowed for approximately by drawing a straight line, like the one shown dotted,

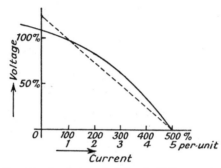

Fig. 16.—Load characteristic of a D.C. generator.

which agrees as nearly as possible with the actual curve over the range of current occurring in the particular problem, and using the values of $k$ and $M$ which would apply for an ideal machine with a series winding having this linear characteristic. In Sect. 13 this method is used to calculate the transient short-circuit current of a D.C. generator.

## 12. Equations for Small Changes or Small Oscillations

The last two types of problem covered by Table 1, page 36, arise when a machine operating under steady conditions is subjected to a small disturbance. If the changes in the variables are small, so that their squares or products can be neglected, the differential equations relating the changes are linear even when the general equations are non-linear. Such equations can be used for studying stability, which depends on the effect of making a small change relative to a steady condition, or for calculating the magnitude of small oscillations which may be superimposed on a condition of steady operation.

In the present section the method of analysing small changes or small oscillations is explained in detail for the simple D.C. machine represented in Fig. 13, for which the equations are

Eqns. (3.9) and (3.11). When $v$ is variable the voltage and torque equations must all be used, and they are non-linear because they contain the products $vi_x$ and $i_x i_a$.

### Differential equations for small changes

Assume that the field voltage changes from a steady value $e_{x0}$ to a slightly different value $e_{x0}+\Delta e_x$, and that all the other variables change similarly. Eqns. (3.9) and (3.11) become:

$$
\left.\begin{aligned}
e_{x0}+\Delta e_x &= (r_f+L_f p)(i_{x0}+\Delta i_x) \\
e_{a0}+\Delta e_a &= M_f(v_0+\Delta v)(i_{x0}+\Delta i_x)+(r_a+L_a p)(i_{a0}+\Delta i_a) \\
f_{t0}+\Delta f_t &= -k_t(i_{x0}+\Delta i_x)(i_{a0}+\Delta i_a)+Jp(v_0+\Delta v)
\end{aligned}\right\}.
$$

$$...(3.16)$$

If the products $\Delta v \Delta i_x$ and $\Delta i_x \Delta i_a$ are neglected, the following linear equations result after subtracting the original equations:

$$
\left.\begin{aligned}
\Delta e_x &= (r_f+L_f p)\Delta i_x \\
\Delta e_a &= M_f v_0 \Delta i_x + M_f i_{x0}\Delta v+(r_a+L_a p)\Delta i_a \\
\Delta f_t &= -k_t i_{x0}\Delta i_a - k_t i_{a0}\Delta i_x + Jp\Delta v
\end{aligned}\right\}. \quad ...(3.17)
$$

It may be noted that the above process is similar to that of differentiation. If, for example, an equation in $x$ and $y$ contains any function $f(x,y)$, the small change in the function is:

$$
\Delta f(x,y) = \frac{\partial f}{\partial x}\Delta x + \frac{\partial f}{\partial y}\Delta y.
$$

Hence the third equation of Eqns. (3.17) could be derived as follows:

$$
\begin{aligned}
\Delta f_t &= -k_t\Delta\{i_x i_a\}+J\Delta\{pv\} \\
&= -k_t(i_x\Delta i_a+i_a\Delta i_x)+Jp\Delta v,
\end{aligned}
$$

after which $i_x$ and $i_a$ are replaced by $i_{x0}$ and $i_{a0}$ to indicate that these are the original steady values. The differentiation is carried out with respect to the dependent variables and not with respect to $t$; hence the operator $p$ is not affected by it. This point is brought out clearly by the long method, based on first principles, used above to derive Eqns. (3.16) and (3.17).

The differential Eqns. (3.17) can be used for studying stability by imagining a sudden small change to be made in any of the applied quantities $e_x$, $e_a$ or $f_t$ and finding the resulting change in $i_x$, $i_a$ or $\nu$. Whichever of these variables is determined, the operational expression for the variable has a denominator of the form $f(p)$ given by the determinant:

$$f(p) = \begin{vmatrix} r_f + L_f p & 0 & 0 \\ M_f \nu_0 & r_q + L_q p & M_f i_{x0} \\ -k_t i_{a0} & -k_t i_{x0} & Jp \end{vmatrix}$$

$$= (r_f + L_f p)\{Jp(r_q + L_q p) + M_f k_t i_{x0}^2\}.$$

For stability the equation $f(p) = 0$ must have no roots with positive real parts, and it can be investigated by any of the well-known stability criteria; for example, Routh's criteria. The application of the method to a simple control system is explained in Sect. 17.

### Vector equations for small oscillations

If the small changes vary sinusoidally with time at a frequency $m/2\pi$, Eqns. (3.17) can be converted into vector equations by replacing $p$ by $jm$, and replacing the instantaneous values $\Delta e_x$, etc., by the complex quantities $\Delta \mathbf{E}_x$, etc. (the small letter is used in the symbol $\Delta \mathbf{v}$). The vector equations, which with a little practice can be written down straight away from the general equations, are:

$$\left.\begin{aligned} \Delta \mathbf{E}_x &= (r_f + jmL_f)\Delta \mathbf{I}_x \\ \Delta \mathbf{E}_a &= M_f \nu_0 \Delta \mathbf{I}_x + M_f i_{x0} \Delta \mathbf{v} + (r_q + jmL_q)\Delta \mathbf{I}_a \\ \Delta \mathbf{F}_t &= -k_t i_{a0}\Delta \mathbf{I}_x - k_t i_{x0}\Delta \mathbf{I}_a + jmJ\Delta \mathbf{v}_- \end{aligned}\right\} \quad \dots(3.18)$$

A D.C. generator driven by a diesel engine provides a simple example of a problem that can be solved by this method. Assume that the torque pulsates at a frequency $m/2\pi$ and that the armature and field voltages are constant. The torque pulsation, which is superimposed on the normal steady torque, may be represented by a complex number $\Delta \mathbf{F}_t$. The voltage pulsations are zero, and hence $\Delta \mathbf{E}_x = \Delta \mathbf{E}_a = 0$. The first equation

(3.18) shows that $\Delta\mathbf{I}_x$ is also zero (that is, that the flux is constant). The equations reduce to:

$$0 = M_f i_{x0} \Delta\mathbf{v} + (r_q + jmL_q)\Delta\mathbf{I}_a \left.\begin{matrix} \\ \end{matrix}\right\} \quad \dots(3.19)$$
$$\Delta\mathbf{F}_t = jmJ\,\Delta\mathbf{v} - k_t i_{f0}\Delta\mathbf{I}_a$$

$\Delta\mathbf{v}$ and $\Delta\mathbf{I}_a$ determine the magnitude and phase of the pulsations of speed and armature current.

### 13. Sudden Short-circuit of a D.C. Generator

The problem of calculating the transient current in a D.C. generator which is suddenly short-circuited is one of increasing practical importance in connection with the large D.C. machines used in steel mills and elsewhere, and the D.C. supply systems on ships and aircraft (Refs. 46.2 and 49.1). It is an example of the third type of problem in Table 1, page 36. In order to obtain an approximate solution it is assumed that the short circuit is instantaneous and that the speed remains constant after the short circuit.

After the short circuit the armature current rises very rapidly to a high peak and then dies away more slowly to the steady short-circuit value. The field current also rises to a peak and then dies away. Because of the heavy currents involved it is essential to allow for the effect of armature reaction and of the current distribution under the brush. Hence Eqns. (3.13) must be used with constants chosen to fit the conditions as closely as possible.

*Separately excited D.C. generator*

Consider first a generator excited at a constant field voltage and operating unloaded before the short circuit. The effect of the short circuit is to reduce the armature voltage $e_a$ suddenly to zero, while leaving the field voltage unchanged. The constant value of the generator voltage before the short circuit is denoted by $V$. It is required to find how the armature current varies with time after the short circuit. The speed is assumed to remain constant.

The problem is best handled by means of the principle of superposition. The voltages and currents after the short circuit

67

are each equal to the sum of the original value and the change resulting from the short circuit. Thus:

$$i_x = i_{x0} + i_x',$$
$$i_a = i_{a0} + i_a',$$

where $i_{x0}$, $i_{a0}$ are the original currents before the short circuit
   ($i_{a0} = 0$, in the example),
   $i_x'$, $i_a'$ are the superimposed currents.

The field voltage does not change, and hence the superimposed voltage $e_x'$ is zero. On the other hand, the armature voltage is $V$ before the short circuit and changes abruptly to zero at the instant of short circuit. Thus the superimposed voltage is $e_a' = -V1$. Because the equations are linear, they are satisfied by the superimposed quantities, and hence become:

$$\left.\begin{array}{l} 0 = (r_f + L_f p)i_x' + Mpi_a' \\ -V1 = M_f v i_x' + k_s v i_a' + (r_a + L_a p)i_a' + Mpi_x' \end{array}\right\} \quad \ldots(3.20)$$

In this and later examples, the word *original* is used for the values existing before the change takes place, while the word *initial* is used for the value immediately after the change. In the example, the initial values of the superimposed currents are zero, and hence, as stated on page 45, the Heaviside method can be used.

The term $Mpi_x'$ can be neglected and the equations can be rewritten:

$$\left.\begin{array}{l} 0 = r_f(1 + T_f p)i_x' + Mpi_a' \\ -V1 = ki_x' + R(1 + T_a p)i_a' \end{array}\right\}, \quad \ldots(3.21)$$

where $R = r_a + k_s v$,
   $k = M_f v$,
   $T_f = L_f/r_f$ (field time constant),
   $T_a = L_a/R$ (effective armature time constant).

The constants $k_s$ and $M$ must allow for any series winding, for the effective brush shift, and for the armature reaction. While the heavy and rapidly varying transient current flows, the interpoles are practically ineffective because of saturation and because of eddy currents in the iron, which prevent the flux from changing rapidly. For an approximate calculation it is a reasonable assumption that the effective brush position is at the trailing edge of the brush. The effect of armature reaction can only be roughly estimated from the steady characteristic (Fig. 16). Nevertheless the theory can be used for a practical study of the short-circuit performance, although it is best to determine the constants by empirical methods based on test results.

In the present problem, the actual short-circuit current $i_a$ is the same as $i_a'$ because the original current $i_{a0}$ is zero, and it is negative because the machine operates as a generator. The positive value, from Eqns. (3.21), is:

$$i_s = -i_a = \frac{(1 + T_f p)}{(1 + T_a p)(1 + T_f p) - \dfrac{Mkp}{r_f R}} \cdot \frac{V}{R} \mathbf{1}. \quad \ldots(3.22)$$

The solution can be obtained in a simple form by making approximations both in factorising the denominator and in deriving partial fractions, because, in a practical machine, the field time constant $T_f$ is always much greater than the armature time constant $T_a$. The denominator may be written in the form $(1 + T_a' p)(1 + T_f' p)$, where $T_a'$ and $T_f'$ are given approximately by:

$$\left. \begin{array}{l} T_a' = \dfrac{T_a}{\left(1 - \dfrac{Mk}{L_f R}\right)} \\[4mm] T_f' = T_f\left(1 - \dfrac{Mk}{L_f R}\right) \end{array} \right\}. \quad \ldots(3.23)$$

With these values the denominator is equal to:

$$1 + \left(T_a' + T_f - \frac{Mk}{r_f R}\right)p + T_a T_f p^2,$$

whence it can be seen that the error occurs only in the coefficient of $p$. It amounts to the difference between $T_a$ and $T_a'$, which is small compared with $T_f$. This kind of approximation is used several times in the following chapters. The accuracy is ample for practical purposes, and the formulae obtained show much more clearly what is happening than the more complicated exact formulae.

69

The solution can now be evaluated by putting the expression of (3.22) in partial fraction form, as explained on page 46, and using the operational formula (2.22) as follows:

$$i_s = \frac{(1+T_f p)}{(1+T_a'p)(1+T_f'p)} \cdot \frac{V}{R} 1$$

$$= \left[ 1 - \frac{T_f'-T_f}{T_f'-T_a'} \cdot \frac{T_f'p}{1+T_f'p} - \frac{T_a'-T_f}{T_a'-T_f'} \cdot \frac{T_a'p}{1+T_a'p} \right] \frac{V}{R} 1,$$

$$= \left[ 1 - \frac{T_f'-T_f}{T_f'-T_a'} e^{-t/T_f'} - \frac{T_a'-T_f}{T_a'-T_f'} e^{-t/T_a'} \right] \frac{V}{R}. \qquad \ldots(3.24)$$

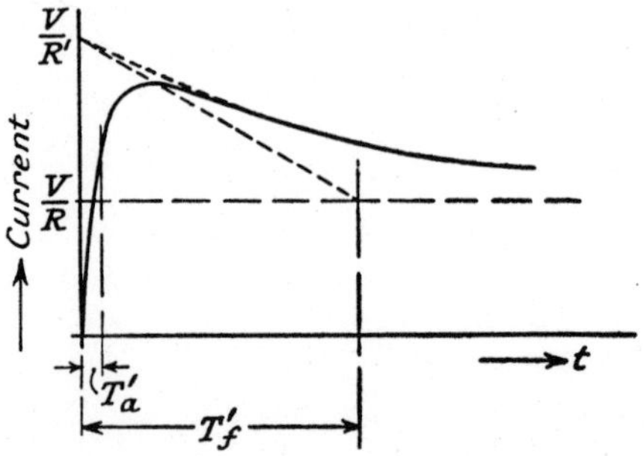

Fig. 17.—Sudden short-circuit current of a D.C. generator.

The result may be simplified by neglecting $T_a'$ compared with $T_f$ or $T_f'$:

$$i_s = \frac{V}{R} + \left( \frac{V}{R'} - \frac{V}{R} \right) \varepsilon^{-t/T_f'} - \frac{V}{R'} \varepsilon^{-t/T_a'}, \qquad \ldots(3.25)$$

where

$$R' = \frac{T_f'}{T_f} R = R - \frac{Mk}{L_f}. \qquad \ldots(3.26)$$

$R'$ is called the *transient resistance*. The time constants $T_a'$ and $T_f'$ can be expressed in terms of $R'$.

$$T_a' = L_a/R',$$
$$T_f' = R'L_f/Rr_f.$$

Fig. 17 (full line) shows a typical curve of short-circuit current plotted from Eqn. (3.25). The upper curve (dotted in the initial portion) represents the sum of the first and second terms, and is what would be obtained if the armature inductance were zero. The current given by this curve rises instantly to $V/R'$ and then dies away to the steady current $V/R$ with time constant $T_f'$. Due to the armature inductance, the actual current rises, not instantaneously but at a rapid rate depending on $T_a'$. The peak value is, however, still given approximately by $V/R'$, but is slightly less. The initial rate of rise is $V/L_a$.

*Self-excited D.C. generator*

The ideal D.C. machine represented by Fig. 15 would, if shunt excited, have a steady short-circuit current equal to zero,

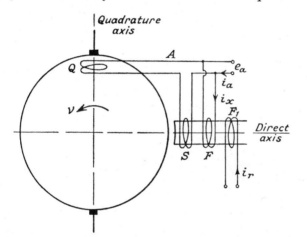

Fig. 18.—Equivalent diagram of a shunt-excited D.C. generator.

because the field would be short-circuited. In practice, however, a current flows in a short-circuited generator because of the residual magnetism. In order to allow for this effect, a constant additional excitation is provided in Fig. 18 by the third field winding $F1$. The winding $F1$ carries a constant current $i_r$, which induces a constant voltage $V_0$ in the winding $Q$.

$i_x$ is small compared with $i_a$, and hence the current in the main circuit may be assumed equal to that at the terminals. With this approximation, the equations are:

$$\left.\begin{aligned} e_x &= (r_f + L_f p)i_x + M p i_a \\ e_a &= k i_x + (R + L_a p)i_a + V_0 \end{aligned}\right\} . \qquad \dots(3.27)$$

71

In the original steady condition, $e_{a0}=V$, and $i_{a0}=0$. Hence:

$$V=r_f i_{x0}=ki_{x0}+V_0 \atop V_0=\dfrac{r_f-k}{r_f}V \quad\Bigg\} . \qquad \text{...(3.28)}$$

The equations for the superimposed currents are:

$$-V\mathbf{1}=(r_f+L_f p)i_x'+Mpi_a',$$
$$-V\mathbf{1}=ki_x'+(R+L_a p)i_a',$$

whence the short-circuit current is:

$$i_s=\frac{(1+T_k p)}{(1+T_a' p)(1+T_f p)}\frac{(r_f-k)}{r_f}\frac{V}{R}\mathbf{1}, \qquad \text{...(3.29)}$$

where $T_k=\dfrac{L_f}{r_f-k}$.

Eqn. (3.29) is of the same form as (3.23), and hence, neglecting $T_a'$ compared with $T_f'$ or $T_k$, the solution is:

$$i_s=\left[1+\left(\frac{T_k}{T_f'}-1\right)\varepsilon^{-t/T_f}-\frac{T_k}{T_f'}\varepsilon^{-t/T_a'}\right]\frac{(r_f-k)}{r_f}\frac{V}{R}$$

$$=\frac{V_0}{R}+\left(\frac{V}{R'}-\frac{V_0}{R}\right)\varepsilon^{-t/T_f'}-\frac{V}{R'}\varepsilon^{-t/T_a'}. \qquad \text{...(3.30)}$$

*Application of the short-circuit theory*

Although the assumptions are such that the results obtained are only approximate, the above theory does give a satisfactory qualitative explanation of the behaviour of a D.C. generator after a short circuit. It is virtually impossible to calculate the constants of a given machine from first principles, but a technique for calculating them can be built up empirically from the analysis of short-circuit tests on a number of different machines. The following example shows how this can be done.

Tests were taken on a 130-volt, 300-amp, shunt-excited generator, and analysed so as to obtain the constants.

*Load test.* $\quad e_a=130, \quad i_a=-300, \quad i_x=3\cdot5.$

*Steady short-circuit test with separate excitation.*

$$e_a=0, \quad i_a=-1500, \quad i_x=3\cdot5.$$

Using these figures in Eqns. (3.27):

$$130 = 3 \cdot 5 r_f,$$
$$130 = 3 \cdot 5k - 300R + V_0,$$
$$0 = 3 \cdot 5k - 1500R + V_0,$$

whence $\quad r_f = 37 \cdot 2, \quad R = 0 \cdot 108, \quad V_0 + 3 \cdot 5k = 162 \cdot 5.$

*Sudden short-circuit test.* The oscillogram of armature current agreed approximately with the following curve:

$$i_s = 730 + 2530\varepsilon^{-t/0 \cdot 089} - 3260\varepsilon^{-t/0 \cdot 0023},$$

giving, by comparison with Eqn. (3.30):

$$V_0/R = 730, \quad V/R' = 3260, \quad T_f' = 0 \cdot 089, \quad T_a' = 0 \cdot 0023,$$

whence $\quad V_0 = 79, \quad k = 21 \cdot 3, \quad R' = 0 \cdot 040, \quad T_f = 0 \cdot 24,$
$\qquad\qquad L_a = 0 \cdot 09 \times 10^{-3}, \quad L_f = 8 \cdot 9, \quad M = 0 \cdot 284.$

# CHAPTER IV

# D.C. Machines in Control Systems

## 14. The D.C. Generator as an Amplifier

The great majority of general supply systems used for the distribution of electrical power operate with alternating current, apart from the relatively small D.C. systems for special purposes such as electric traction, or on ships and aircraft. Nevertheless D.C. machines are still very widely used for industrial purposes where flexibility of control is important (Ref. 52.3). For drives requiring accurate and rapid automatic control, equipments comprising a number of D.C. generators and motors operating in conjunction with regulating devices of various kinds are in frequent and increasing use. The study of automatic control systems covers a wide field, and this chapter is only concerned with the part played by the D.C. machine in such systems.

It is important to be able to analyse a control system with reasonable accuracy under both steady and transient conditions. Since, however, the system may include several D.C. machines as well as other apparatus, the representation of each individual element must be fairly simple; otherwise the analysis of the complete system becomes too complicated. The method in general use depends on the conception of each D.C. machine or other element in the system as an amplifier. The complete system is built up as a chain of amplifying stages interconnected so as to obtain the desired performance.

In the following pages the simplified methods of representation are explained with reference to the more general treatment of Chaps. II and III. As before, the basis of the method is the setting up of differential equations from which the performance can be calculated.

### D.C. generators and exciters

For a generator or exciter supplying a definite external circuit it is assumed that the speed is constant and that the armature impedance can be included with that of the external circuit. The simplified representation of Fig. 13 is used and the internal voltage $e_2 = M_f \nu i_x$ is taken to be the output voltage. This output voltage is controlled by the field voltage $e_x$, denoted now by $e_1$. The simplified D.C. machine, represented diagrammatically by Fig. 19, is considered as an amplifier whose output voltage $e_2$ is controlled by the input voltage $e_1$. From Eqns. (3.9) it follows that:

$$e_2 = \frac{K}{1+Tp} \cdot e_1, \qquad \qquad ...(4.1)$$

where $K = \dfrac{M_f \nu}{r_f}$ (D.C. voltage ratio),

$T = \dfrac{L_f}{r_f}$ (field time constant).

If one D.C. machine is used as an exciter to excite another generator, as in Fig. 20, the output voltage $e_3$ of the combination is related to the input voltage $e_1$ by:

$$e_3 = \frac{K_1}{1+T_1 p} \cdot \frac{K_2}{1+T_2 p} \cdot e_1, \qquad \qquad ...(4.2)$$

where the suffixes of $K$ and $T$ correspond to the two machines.

Considering the combination of two D.C. generators as a two-stage amplifier, the field of the first machine is the input circuit of the amplifier and is used to control the output. The power required to provide the output power and the losses is of course supplied by the motor driving the generators. In any D.C. generator the output power is always much greater than the field power, and their ratio is called its *power amplification*. By using a chain of several D.C. generators a large overall power amplification, which is the product of the individual amplifications, may be obtained.

### Build-up curves of D.C. generators

The *build-up curve* is defined as the curve showing the variation of output voltage with time when the controlling field winding is suddenly switched on to a constant voltage, or when the resistance of the field winding is suddenly reduced. For a single ideal generator, as in Fig. 19, the build-up curve after switching an unexcited machine on to a field voltage $V$ is obtained by solving Eqn. (4.1) with $e_1$ put equal to the step-function voltage $V\mathbf{1}$. The solution is:

$$e_2 = KV(1 - \varepsilon^{-t/T}). \qquad \ldots(4.3)$$

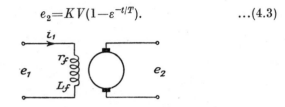

Fig. 19.—D.C. generator considered as an amplifier.

The curve shown by the full line in Fig. 21 is an exponential curve having time constant $T$ and final value $KV$. The time constant of an exponential curve is the time in which the final

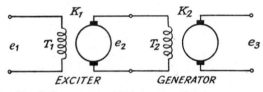

Fig. 20.—D.C. generator and exciter considered as a two-stage amplifier.

value would be reached if the initial rate of change were maintained, as indicated by the tangent line at the origin.

For two D.C. generators, connected as in Fig. 20, the build-up

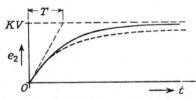

Fig. 21.—Build-up curve of a D.C. generator.

curve is no longer a simple exponential curve but is like that shown by the full line in Fig. 22. If an exponential curve approximating as closely as possible to the actual curve is drawn, as shown by the heavy dotted line in Fig. 22, it is found that the effective time constant is very roughly equal to the

76

sum of the individual time constants. Hence it is often a good enough approximation merely to take the build-up curve as a simple exponential curve for which the time constant is $T_1 + T_2$.

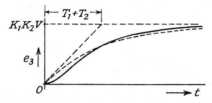

FIG. 22.—Build-up curve of a D.C. generator
with an exciter.

The change in the output voltage lags behind the change in the input voltage causing it. The time delay is usually an adverse factor in control systems and, even apart from considerations of stability, it is desirable to keep the time constant as small as possible.

*Build-up curve of a saturated exciter*

By suddenly increasing the voltage applied to its field an exciter may be used to force up the excitation of an alternator rapidly, if for any reason the voltage tends to fall; the saturation of the exciter is then often an important factor. The build-up curve of a saturated exciter on open-circuit can be calculated by a numerical step-by-step computation if the saturation curve is known (Ref. 34.1). For the unsaturated condition Eqns. (4.1) can be put in the form:

$$e_1 = \frac{e_2}{K} + \frac{Tpe_2}{K}$$

$$= r_f i_x + \frac{T}{K} \frac{de_2}{dt}.$$

The second term states that the induced voltage is equal to a constant times the rate of change of the flux, which is proportional to $e_2$. The above equation therefore holds also for saturated conditions and hence:

$$\Delta t = \frac{T}{K} \frac{1}{e_1 - r_f i_x} \cdot \Delta e_2, \qquad \ldots (4.4)$$

where $\Delta t$ and $\Delta e_2$ are small increments of time and voltage. If the voltage $e_2$ at any instant is known, the corresponding value of $i_x$ can be read from the saturation curve and the increment $\Delta e_2$ corresponding to an interval $\Delta t$ can be calculated from Eqn. (4.4). In this way the build-up curve, starting from any known initial condition, can be calculated step by step. The dotted curve of Fig. 21, when compared with the full-line curve, shows the effect of saturation on the build-up curve for a machine which was previously unexcited. More often the build-up curve is required for a generator which already has some excitation.

Books and specifications often refer to 'the response curve of an exciter' (Ref. 44.2). The response is, however, not determined definitely unless the initial and final field voltages, as well as the amount of the field resistance in circuit, are clearly specified. Moreover the term usually relates to the open-circuit response curve. A more important curve for practical purposes is the one obtained when the exciter is connected to the field of a larger generator, when armature reaction must be considered as well as saturation.

### 15. Cross-field Generators

A cross-field D.C. machine is a special machine with brushes located both on the direct axis and on the quadrature axis, as in Fig. 4. Cross-field machines are often used as amplifying generators in control systems, because they can be designed to have a high power amplification ratio as well as a relatively small time delay (Refs. 47.2 and 54.1). Fig. 23 shows the diagram of an idealised cross-field D.C. generator (amplidyne or metadyne) for use in a control system. The diagram shows the actual circuits through the brushes, and also the pseudo-stationary coils $D$ and $Q$ which replace them. The quadrature circuit $Q$ is short-circuited and the main output voltage is obtained from the direct-axis coil $D$. The machine has a field winding $F$ on the direct axis, and there is no stator winding on the quadrature axis. Otherwise the machine is like that represented in Fig. 4.

During steady D.C. operation the direct-axis flux due to the field current $i_f$ induces a rotational voltage between the quadrature brushes. Since the quadrature brushes are short-circuited there flows a quadrature current $i_q$, which sets up a flux on the quadrature axis and induces a voltage between the main (direct-axis) brushes. When a load current flows, the direct-axis flux is due to the combined effect of $i_f$ and $i_d$. It may be noted that a positive field current produces a positive output voltage $e_d$, and there is no need to use the symbols $e_x$ and $i_x$, which were introduced in Fig. 13 in order to avoid a negative sign in Eqns. (3.9).

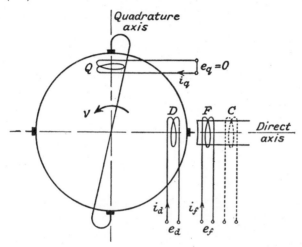

Fig. 23.—Diagram of a cross-field D.C. generator.

The general equations for the three coils are:

$$\left.\begin{aligned}
e_f &= (r_f + L_f p)i_f + M_{df}p i_d \\
e_d &= M_{df}p i_f + (r_d + L_d p)i_d + M_q v i_q \\
0 &= -M_f v i_f - M_d v i_d + (r_q + L_q p)i_q
\end{aligned}\right\} . \qquad \ldots (4.5)$$

The equations are obtained from Eqns. (2.2) by omitting the fourth equation and the fourth row of the impedance matrix, and putting $e_q$ equal to zero.

It is usual to provide a compensating winding $C$ (indicated by the dotted coil in Fig. 23) connected in series with the main brushes in order to reduce the effect of the M.M.F. set up by the current $i_d$. To allow for this, the constants $M_d$, $r_d$, $L_d$ and

$M_{df}$ in Eqns. (4.5) must be modified. For a *fully compensated machine*, in which the compensating winding exactly neutralises the armature M.M.F., the constants $M_d$ and $M_{df}$ are zero. Putting $e_f = e_1$, and the internal voltage $[e_d - (r_d + L_d p)i_d]$ equal to $e_2$, the equations for the fully compensated machine reduce to:

$$e_2 = \frac{M_q v}{r_q + L_q p} \frac{M_f v}{r_f + L_f p} \cdot e_1. \qquad \ldots(4.6)$$

With a given speed these equations are of the same form as Eqns. (4.2) for the two D.C. generators. Hence a fully compensated cross-field generator is equivalent to a combination of two ordinary generators, and gives a correspondingly high power amplification. It has two time constants, one for the field circuit and one for the quadrature circuit.

An *under-compensated* or an *over-compensated* cross-field generator differs from the fully compensated machine because there are additional voltages depending on the load current $i_d$. The effect under steady conditions is similar to that of a series compounding winding on an ordinary generator.

### 16. D.C. Motors in Control Systems

A typical electrical control system comprises a main machine, which may be either a generator or a motor, and a number of auxiliary machines or control devices used to control the main machine. When the main machine is a motor, it is coupled to the machinery which forms the mechanical load, and the function of the control system is to control its speed in relation to the torque required for any condition of operation. Auxiliary motors are also often used for operating control devices other than electrical machines.

D.C. motors may be controlled in one of two ways:

(a) Field voltage control.
(b) Armature voltage control.

For either method, or for any combination of the two methods, Eqns. (3.9) and (3.11) hold, and may often be simplified for particular cases. With field control, which is carried out by varying the field with the armature voltage held constant, the equations are complicated by the fact that both armature and field currents vary and that the products $vi_f$ and $i_f i_q$ occur in them. A complete solution is therefore only possible by numerical computation, which may be cumbersome if the system contains many elements. A useful analysis of stability, or of the operation during small changes, can be made by the method explained in Sect. 12.

Fortunately, the commonest method of control of D.C. motors, particularly in the more complicated systems for which an accurate analysis is important, is by armature voltage control, using the *Ward-Leonard system*. In this type of system the field voltage, and hence the field current is constant while the armature voltage is varied. The equations can then be simplified considerably.

### D.C. motor with armature voltage control

Fig. 24 represents a motor with a constant field current $i_x$, having its speed $v$ controlled by the armature voltage $e_q$ now

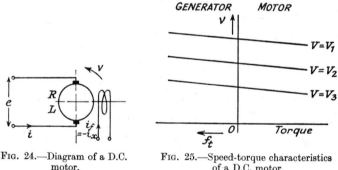

Fig. 24.—Diagram of a D.C.     Fig. 25.—Speed-torque characteristics
    motor.                        of a D.C. motor.

denoted by $e$. Eqns. (3.9) and (3.11) reduce to:

$$\left.\begin{array}{l} e = k_1 v + (R + Lp)i \\ f_t = Jpv - k_2 i \end{array}\right\}, \qquad \ldots(4.7)$$

where $k_1 = M_f i_x =$ voltage per radian per second,

$\quad k_2 = k_t i_x =$ torque per unit armature current.

Under steady conditions with constant applied voltage $V$, the torque-speed curve is given by:

$$v = \frac{V}{k_1} + \frac{R}{k_1 k_2} f_t. \qquad \ldots(4.8)$$

81

The steady speed-torque characteristics of the motor for different values of $V$ are shown in Fig. 25. The positive value of $f_t$, corresponding to generator operation, is plotted to the left in order to show the diagram in the usual form, as applied to a separately excited motor. For the idealised machine the curves are straight lines on which the speed falls slightly as the motoring torque increases.

Under transient conditions the speed is given by:

$$v = \frac{\dfrac{e}{k_1} + \dfrac{T_m}{J}(1+Tp)f_t}{1+T_m p(1+Tp)}, \qquad \ldots(4.9)$$

where $T = L/R$ (armature time constant),

$T_m = \dfrac{JR}{k_1 k_2}$ (mechanical time constant).

The transient analysis of a control system is usually made for the condition when the applied torque is zero. Alternatively, if there is a constant applied torque, the variables in Eqn. (4.9) are taken to be superimposed changes of voltage, torque and speed. Thus in either case, $f_t = 0$. Moreover the electrical time constant $T$ is usually much smaller than the mechanical time constant $T_m$. Hence approximately:

$$v = \frac{1}{(1+Tp)(1+T_m p)} \frac{e}{k_1}. \qquad \ldots(4.10)$$

Thus a motor with armature voltage control can be considered as a combination of an electrical stage with time constant $T$ and a mechanical stage with time constant $T_m$. For many purposes the inductance $L$ can be neglected entirely, giving:

$$v = \frac{1}{(1+T_m p)} \frac{e}{k_1}. \qquad \ldots(4.11)$$

If, as an example, the motor when unloaded is suddenly switched on to a constant voltage, the speed rises exponentially with time constant $T_m$.

### 17. The Analysis of Control Systems

A control system is built up of several elements, each of which acts as an amplifying stage, in such a way that a large output is controlled by a much smaller *control input*. In a *closed-loop system* the output voltage or other quantity is connected, or *fed back*, to the input circuit in such a way as to improve the accuracy and rapidity of response of the system. A closed-loop control system is analysed by obtaining the differential equation which governs its operation (Ref. 51.3). Two examples are discussed in this section.

*Ward-Leonard equipment with speed regulator*

Fig. 26 is a diagram of a control system for regulating the speed of a D.C. motor. The motor has a constant field current

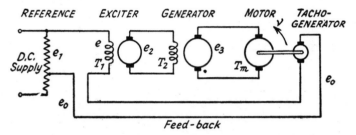

Fig. 26.—Diagram of a Ward-Leonard speed-control system.

and is supplied by a generator, driven at constant speed and having an exciter as shown. The diagram would also apply if an amplidyne were used instead of the combination of a generator and an exciter. The motor speed is controlled by the field voltage $e$ of the exciter. A tachometer generator coupled to the motor produces a voltage proportional to the speed, and, in order to obtain an automatic regulation of the speed, the tachometer voltage $e_0$ is fed back to the input end of the amplifying system. It is connected in opposition to a constant but adjustable D.C. reference voltage $e_1$ obtained from a potentiometer, and the difference between the two voltages $e_0$ and $e_1$ is the voltage $e$ used to supply the exciter field. Because $e$ is much smaller than $e_1$, the output voltage $e_0$ cannot differ greatly from the reference voltage $e_1$ under any steady condition of operation. Hence an accurate regulation of the motor speed is obtained.

From Eqns. (4.2) and (4.11) the following relation holds, since $e_0$ is proportional to the speed $v$.

$$e_0 = \frac{K}{(1 + T_1 p)(1 + T_2 p)(1 + T_m p)} \cdot e, \qquad \ldots(4.12)$$

where $K$ is a constant.

Also $e = e_1 - e_0$. Hence:

$$e_0 = \frac{K}{(1 + T_1 p)(1 + T_2 p)(1 + T_m p) + K} \cdot e_1. \qquad \ldots(4.13)$$

Eqn. (4.13) is the differential equation of the system and can be used to calculate the steady or transient behaviour or to study its stability. Although the above example is a simple one, the equation is typical of those obtained in the analysis of closed-loop control systems.

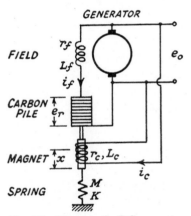

FIG. 27.—Diagram of a D.C. generator with a carbon-pile regulator.

### D.C. generator with carbon-pile voltage regulator

Fig. 27 is a diagram of a system in which the voltage of a D.C. generator is regulated by means of a carbon-pile regulator. The carbon pile has a non-linear characteristic such that the voltage $e_r$ across the pile varies with the displacement $x$ and the current $i_f$ according to the function $f(x, i_f)$. The constants of the system are as follows:

$k_f$ = generator voltage per unit field current,
$r_f$, $L_f$ = resistance, inductance of the generator field,
$r_c$, $L_c$ = resistance, inductance of the regulator coil,
$k_c$ = force on the regulator for unit current in the coil,
$K$ = spring constant of the regulator,
$M$ = mass of the moving parts of the regulator.

The armature impedance of the machine and the damping in the regulator are neglected.

If a small disturbing external force $f_m$ is applied to the magnet, the following three differential equations are obtained for the field circuit, the regulator coil circuit, and the mechanical system of the regulator:

$$\left.\begin{array}{l} k_f i_f = (r_f + L_f p)i_f + f(x,\ i_f) \\ k_f i_f = (r_c + L_c p)i_c \\ f_m = (K + Mp^2)x - k_c i_c \end{array}\right\} . \qquad \ldots(4.14)$$

By eliminating $i_c$, the number of equations is reduced to two:

$$\left.\begin{array}{l} 0 = f(x,\ i_f) + (r_f - k_f + L_f p)i_f \\ f_m = (K + Mp^2)x - \dfrac{k_c k_f}{(r_c + L_c p)}\, i_f \end{array}\right\} . \qquad \ldots(4.15)$$

The two non-linear differential equations (4.15) can be used to determine $x$ and $i_f$ if the applied force is known. For small changes $\Delta x$, $\Delta i_f$, relative to steady values $x_0$, $i_{f0}$, they become:

$$\left.\begin{array}{l} 0 = \left[\dfrac{\partial f}{\partial x}\right]_0 \Delta x + \left[\dfrac{\partial f}{\partial i_f}\right]_0 \Delta i_f + (r_f - k_f + L_f p)\Delta i_f \\ \Delta f_m = (K + Mp^2)\Delta x - \dfrac{k_c k_f}{(r_c + L_c p)}\, \Delta i_f \end{array}\right\} , \qquad \ldots(4.16)$$

where $\left[\dfrac{\partial f}{\partial x}\right]_0$ and $\left[\dfrac{\partial f}{\partial i_f}\right]_0$ are the values of the partial derivatives for the steady condition.

For small oscillations at frequency $m/2\pi$ due to a force pulsation represented by the complex number $\Delta \mathbf{F}_m$, Eqns. (4.16) can be converted into vector equations, in which the pulsations of field current and regulator displacement are represented by complex numbers $\Delta \mathbf{I}_f$ and $\Delta \mathbf{X}$.

$$\left.\begin{array}{l} 0 = \left[\dfrac{\partial f}{\partial x}\right]_0 \Delta \mathbf{X} + \left[\dfrac{\partial f}{\partial i_f}\right]_0 \Delta \mathbf{I}_f + (r_f - k_f + jmL_f)\Delta \mathbf{I}_f \\ \Delta \mathbf{F}_m = (K - m^2 M)\Delta \mathbf{X} - \dfrac{k_c k_f}{(r_c + jmL_c)}\, \Delta \mathbf{I}_f \end{array}\right\} . \qquad \ldots(4.17)$$

Equations (4.16) can be used to study the stability of the system using any of the well-known criteria. Eqns. (4.17) can be used to determine the magnitude and phase of the oscillations of current and displacement caused by a given force pulsation. A similar problem is analysed by matrix methods in Ref. 40.1.

# CHAPTER V

# The Steady-State Vector Diagrams
# of A.C. Machines

## 18. Representation of Sinusoidal M.M.F. and Flux Waves by Space Vectors

Before deriving the general operational equations of A.C. machines it is worth while to consider briefly the special case of steady operation, which can be analysed independently by means of vector equations and diagrams. The method used in this chapter, which is essentially the same for the different types of A.C. machine, follows the same lines as the later development of the general theory, but is a good deal simpler. The present chapter forms a link between the usual textbook treatment and the general treatment which is the main theme of the book.

The theory starts with the currents flowing in the various windings of the machine and determines first the M.M.F. and then the flux produced by the currents. From the flux, the voltages induced in the windings are calculated and hence the vector diagrams or equations are obtained. For an A.C. machine operating under steady conditions with balanced polyphase voltages and currents, the fundamental flux density wave rotates round the air-gap at constant speed relative to the A.C. winding; that is, it is a *rotating flux wave*. The steady-state vector diagrams are based on a consideration of the rotating waves of M.M.F. and flux produced by the polyphase currents.

The vectors considered in the earlier chapters are called *time vectors*, because the quantity represented varies sinusoidally with time. *Space vectors* on the other hand represent quantities which vary sinusoidally in space; for example, the fundamental M.M.F. along the air-gap line. At any instant a sinusoidal wave of M.M.F. can be represented by a space vector with its axis at the point of maximum M.M.F.; if two or more such waves are stationary or rotate at the same speed, they can be added by vector addition.

A space vector of M.M.F. is defined by a complex number **M** which is related to the space distribution of the M.M.F. in the same way as a time vector of current defined by the complex number **I** is related to the time variation of the current (see Eqns. (2.9). Fig. 28 is a developed diagram showing the variation of the M.M.F. with the angle $\theta$. If $M_m$ is the maximum M.M.F., the value of the M.M.F. at the point $\theta$ is:

$$m = M_m \cos(\theta + \varphi) = Re\{\mathbf{M}\varepsilon^{j\theta}\}, \qquad \ldots(5.1)$$

where $\mathbf{M} = M_m \varepsilon^{j\varphi}$.

Thus **M** is a complex number analogous to that used for a time vector, except that, following the usual practice, the

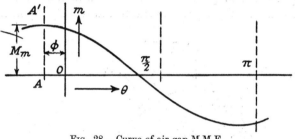

Fig. 28.—Curve of air-gap M.M.F.

magnitude of the space vector is taken to be equal to the maximum value, rather than the R.M.S. value, so that the factor $\sqrt{2}$ does not appear in Eqn. (5.1). For the machines dealt with in the present chapter the flux and M.M.F. waves are represented by space vectors, while the voltages and currents are represented by time vectors. It is important to distinguish between the two kinds of vectors.

The voltage induced in a coil by a rotating or stationary flux wave is proportional to the flux and to the relative speed between the flux and the coil. The time phase of the voltage depends on the space position of the flux wave relative to the coil. Hence the time vector representing the induced voltage is directly related to the space vector representing the flux.

When a machine has a uniform air-gap, the air-gap flux density is everywhere proportional to the M.M.F., and the induced voltage can be obtained directly from the M.M.F. In a salient-pole machine, on the other hand, the proportionality no longer holds. When, however, the M.M.F. wave rotates at the same speed as the poles, it can be resolved into two components, one along each axis. The corresponding components of the flux wave can then be found as explained on page 21. The usual theory of the cylindrical-rotor synchronous machine and of the induction motor does not depend on resolving the flux into axis components and is thus a true *rotating field theory*. On the other hand, the salient-pole synchronous machine requires a *two-axis theory*.

### 19. The Induction Motor

Fig. 29 is a diagram of a two-pole induction motor having phase coils $A_1$, $B_1$, $C_1$ on the stator and $A_2$, $B_2$, $C_2$ on the rotor

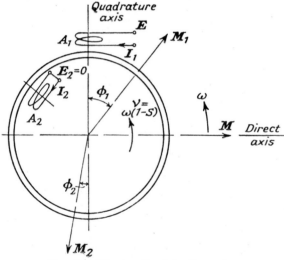

FIG. 29.—Diagram of an induction motor.

(for clearness only $A_1$ and $A_2$ are shown). Coil $A_1$ is stationary on the quadrature axis, while coil $A_2$ rotates with the rotor at the constant speed $\omega(1-s)$, where $\omega$ is the synchronous speed and $s$ is the slip. During steady operation the M.M.F. and flux waves due to the balanced polyphase currents in either winding rotate relative to the stator at synchronous speed $\omega$.

Consider the instant at which the resultant M.M.F. wave, represented by the space vector $\mathbf{M}$, is on the direct axis (drawn horizontally), as indicated on Fig. 29. At the same instant, the component M.M.F.s due to the primary and secondary currents respectively are represented by the space vectors $\mathbf{M_1}$ and $\mathbf{M_2}$ at angles $(-\varphi_1)$ and $(180° - \varphi_2)$ to the vertical. The three vectors move round together at speed $\omega$ and are related by the vector diagram (Fig. 30(a)).

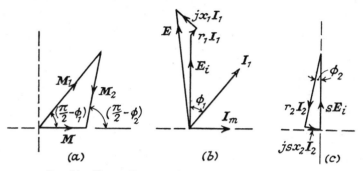

FIG. 30.—Vector diagrams of a polyphase induction motor.
(a) Space vector diagram of M.M.F.s.
(b) Time vector diagram of primary voltages.
(c) Time vector diagram of secondary voltages.

If core losses are neglected, the resultant flux wave due to $\mathbf{M}$ also has its axis on the direct axis, and consequently the internal voltage, opposing that induced in the primary phase $A_1$, has its maximum value at the instant considered. The internal voltage is represented by the vector $\mathbf{E}_i$. If the primary windings carried polyphase currents such that the current in phase $A_1$ was in phase with $\mathbf{E}_i$, they would set up an M.M.F. on the quadrature axis at this instant. Since, however, the vector $\mathbf{M_1}$ is displaced by $\varphi_1$ from the vertical axis, the corresponding primary current $\mathbf{I_1}$ actually lags behind $\mathbf{E}_i$ by the angle $\varphi_1$ (see Fig. 30(b)). In the primary voltage vector diagram of Fig. 30(b), which applies to phase $A_1$, the terminal voltage $\mathbf{E}$ is the sum of the internal voltage $\mathbf{E}_i$, the resistance drop $r_1\mathbf{I_1}$ and the leakage reactance drop $jx_1\mathbf{I_1}$.

The secondary winding is not located in any definite position relative to the primary winding, and in general has a different number of turns per phase. If a per-unit system, defined for the stationary induction motor in the same way as for the transformer on page 17, is used, the voltage induced in phase $A_2$ by the resultant flux has the same magnitude as $\mathbf{E}_i$ if the rotor is at rest. With a slip $s$ the flux induces a slip-frequency voltage, the magnitude of which is $s$ times that of the primary induced voltage, while the phase depends on the rotor position. In Fig. 30(c) the vector $s\mathbf{E}_i$, like $\mathbf{E}_i$ in Fig. 30(b), represents the voltage opposing the induced voltage. If the secondary winding carried polyphase currents such that the current in phase $A_2$ was in phase with the secondary induced voltage, the secondary currents would set up an M.M.F. on the quadrature axis at the instant when the flux is along the direct axis. This relation holds whatever the actual position of the secondary winding may be at that instant. Since, for the operating condition indicated in Fig. 29, $\mathbf{M}_2$ is displaced from the quadrature axis by the angle $(\pi - \varphi_2)$, it follows that the secondary current vector $\mathbf{I}_2$ is displaced by $(\pi - \varphi_2)$ from $s\mathbf{E}_i$, as shown in the time vector diagram of Fig. 30(c). In the secondary voltage vector diagram (Fig. 30(c)), the sum of $s\mathbf{E}_i$, the resistance drop $r_2\mathbf{I}_2$, and the leakage reactance drop $jsx_2\mathbf{I}_2$, is zero, since the secondary winding is short-circuited.

The theory of the induction motor is thus based on three separate vector diagrams:

1. Space vector diagram of M.M.F.s.
2. Time vector diagram of primary voltages at supply frequency.
3. Time vector diagram of secondary voltages at slip frequency.

When a per-unit system is used, the primary and secondary M.M.F.s are in the ratio of the currents producing them. The current in the primary winding which would produce the resultant M.M.F. is called the *magnetising current*, and the vector is denoted by $\mathbf{I}_m$. It lags 90° behind $\mathbf{E}_i$ and is therefore horizontal in Fig. 30(b). Fig. 30(a) may be considered as a current diagram showing that $\mathbf{I}_m$ is the sum of $\mathbf{I}_1$ and $\mathbf{I}_2$, since each M.M.F. vector is proportional to the corresponding current vector.

The vector equations can be written down from the diagrams (Figs. 30(a) to 30(c)). The quotient of the magnitudes of $\mathbf{E}_i$ and

$\mathbf{I}_m$ is a constant called the magnetising reactance $X_m$. The equations are:

$$\left.\begin{aligned}
\mathbf{E} &= \mathbf{E}_i + (r_1 + jx_1)\mathbf{I}_1 \\
0 &= s\mathbf{E}_i + (r_2 + jsx_2)\mathbf{I}_2 \\
\mathbf{I}_m &= \mathbf{I}_1 + \mathbf{I}_2 \\
\mathbf{E}_i &= jX_m\mathbf{I}_m
\end{aligned}\right\} . \qquad \ldots(5.2)$$

Elimination of $\mathbf{E}_i$ and $\mathbf{I}_m$ from these equations gives the two voltage equations of the induction motor:

$$\left.\begin{aligned}
\mathbf{E} &= \{r_1 + j(X_m + x_1)\}\mathbf{I}_1 + jX_m\mathbf{I}_2 \\
0 &= jsX_m\mathbf{I}_1 + \{r_2 + js(X_m + x_2)\}\mathbf{I}_2
\end{aligned}\right\} . \qquad \ldots(5.3)$$

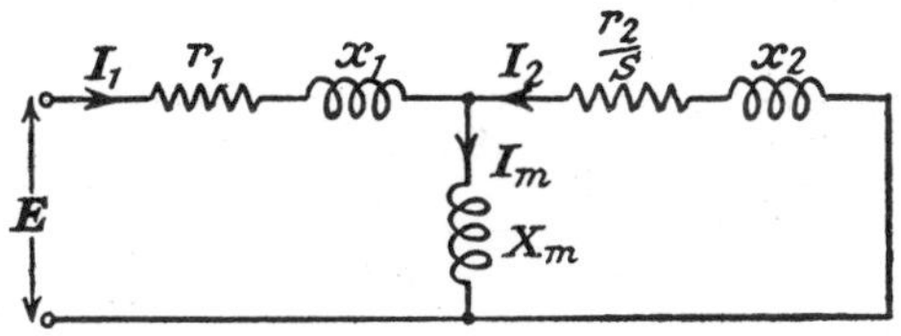

Fig. 31.—Equivalent circuit of an induction motor.

It may be noted that Eqns. (5.3) are similar to those of the transformer. If Eqns. (1.2) are converted into vector equations, and new symbols are introduced for the reactances, they correspond exactly to Eqns. (5.3), except for the presence of the slip $s$. With the motor at rest ($s=1$) the equations become identical with those of the transformer.

Fig. 31 shows an *equivalent circuit* of the induction motor. An equivalent circuit of a machine may be defined as a system of static elements in which the currents and voltages satisfy the same equations as the machine. It is evident that Eqns. (5.3) apply to the network shown in Fig. 31. It may be noted that the direction of $\mathbf{I}_2$ is opposite to that usually shown in textbooks.

## 20. The Cylindrical-rotor Synchronous Machine

Fig. 32 is a diagram of a two-pole synchronous machine having a field winding $F$ on the outer member and a three-phase winding on the inner rotating member. In a practical machine, particularly in a large generator, the field system is almost always on the rotor, but in the diagram of the idealised machine it is indicated on the stator and its axis is taken as the direct

91

axis. The term 'cylindrical-rotor machine' applies to a machine, like a turbo-alternator, in which the field element on the rotor has no salient poles, but for the purposes of the theory the term is used for any synchronous machine with a uniform air-gap.

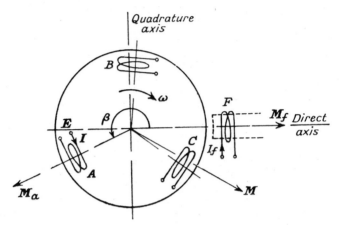

Fig. 32.—Diagram of a synchronous machine.

The damper windings shown on Fig. 3 are omitted in Fig. 32 because they do not affect the operation under steady conditions. The lettering of the armature coils is in the same sequence as in Fig. 3.

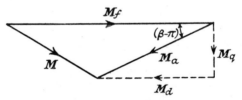

Fig. 33.—Space vector diagram of M.M.F.s in a synchronous machine.

Fig. 32, as well as Figs. 33 to 37, apply for steady operation of the machine as a generator at lagging power factor. The rotor runs at the constant synchronous speed $\omega$, and it is assumed that the direction of rotation is clockwise, so that $\nu = -\omega$. The armature winding carries balanced polyphase currents, the phase sequence of which must be $C$–$B$–$A$. The clockwise rotation is chosen in order, as explained later, to make the angular relations in the space vector diagram of M.M.F.s (Fig. 33) correspond to those in the voltage diagram (Fig. 34), when drawn according to the usual convention.

The M.M.F. wave due to the armature currents rotates counter-clockwise relative to the armature at speed $\omega$, and is therefore in a fixed position in space whatever the position of the armature. The position of the armature winding is specified by the angle $\theta$ which the axis of coil $A$ makes with the direct axis, and in Fig. 32 the windings are shown in the position they occupy at the instant when the current in phase $A$ is a maximum. At this instant $\theta$ has the value $\beta$, which is greater than 180°. The axis of the armature M.M.F. coincides with the axis of phase $A$ at this instant, and hence the M.M.F. vector $\mathbf{M}_a$, which remains fixed as the armature rotates, is in the position shown.

In the diagram, the M.M.F. vector due to the field current $\mathbf{I}_f$ is along the direct axis. The resultant M.M.F. obtained by adding $\mathbf{M}_a$ and $\mathbf{M}_f$ is represented by the vector $\mathbf{M}$. The space vector diagram (Fig. 33) shows the relation between the three M.M.F. vectors.

Because the machine has a uniform air-gap, the resultant flux density is proportional to the M.M.F. at every point, and the flux can be considered to be the resultant of two component fluxes proportional to $\mathbf{M}_a$ and $\mathbf{M}_f$. Moreover the voltage induced in phase $A$ is proportional to the flux, and its time phase depends on the space position of the flux, so that the voltage can be considered to be the resultant of two corresponding component voltages. Hence the space vector diagram of M.M.F.s can be converted into the time vector diagram of voltages given by the triangle $OST$ in Fig. 34.

In Fig. 34, $OS$ is the vector $\mathbf{E}_0$ representing the voltage induced in phase $A$ by the component of flux due to the field current. It is proportional to $\mathbf{M}_f$ and is drawn vertically because the voltage is maximum when coil $A$ has its axis vertical. $\mathbf{E}_0$ is thus the open-circuit voltage, which depends only on the field current. $ST$ represents the voltage induced by the component of flux due to the armature current $\mathbf{I}$, and can be considered as a reactive drop in the *magnetising reactance* $x_{md}$. It leads the

93

current by 90° and is equal to $jx_{md}\mathbf{I}$. Finally, $OT$ represents the internal voltage $\mathbf{E}_i$ induced by the resultant flux. The voltage triangle $OST$ is similar to the M.M.F. triangle in Fig. 33 but is turned through 90°.

The voltage vector diagram is completed by adding the resistance drop $r_a\mathbf{I}$ and the leakage reactance drop $jX_a\mathbf{I}$ to the internal voltage $\mathbf{E}_i$. The resultant is equal to the terminal voltage $\mathbf{E}$, which makes an angle $\alpha$ with the horizontal axis. Fig. 34 is the complete vector diagram relating the terminal voltage $\mathbf{E}$ and the current $\mathbf{I}$.

Although the vector diagram has been derived for the particular condition when the machine is operating as a generator at lagging power factor, the theory

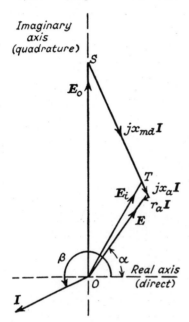

Fig. 34.—Vector diagram of a cylindrical-rotor synchronous machine.

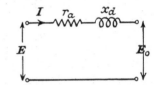

Fig. 35.—Equivalent circuit of a cylindrical-rotor synchronous machine.

is quite general and applies for any condition of steady operation. The shape of the diagram does of course vary considerably at different loads and power factors. Alternatively the relations given by the vector diagram may be expressed by a vector equation or by an equivalent circuit. The equation is:

$$\mathbf{E}=\mathbf{E}_0+(r_a+jx_d)\mathbf{I}, \qquad \ldots(5.4)$$

where $x_d = x_{md} + x_a$ (synchronous reactance).

The equivalent circuit of the cylindrical-rotor synchronous machine is shown in Fig. 35. It is evident that Eqn. (5.4) applies to this network.

The terminal voltage (less the resistance drop) is determined as the sum of $\mathbf{E}_0$, the voltage that would be induced if only $\mathbf{I}_f$ were present, and $jx_a\mathbf{I}$ the voltage that would be induced if only $\mathbf{I}$ were present. The result is based on the principle of superposition, which depends on the assumption of linearity. The voltage $jx_a\mathbf{I}$ is that induced in the armature by the total flux set up by the armature current $\mathbf{I}$, when this current acts alone. It is sometimes stated that the synchronous reactance is a fictitious quantity, but this conception is quite out of keeping with the modern viewpoint. Actually the synchronous reactance $x_d$ is less fictitious than the leakage reactance $x_a$, because $x_d$ is the complete reactance of the armature winding whereas $x_a$ is only a part of it (see page 19).

For the synchronous machine all the reactances are denoted by small letters. This departure from the notation suggested on page 19 is made because the use of small letters for the reactances of synchronous machines is well established in the literature. Moreover some of the derived reactances, like the transient reactances (page 123), are intermediate between complete and leakage reactances, and it would be difficult to decide whether a capital or a small symbol should be used.

### 21. The Salient-pole Synchronous Machine

For a machine with salient poles, indicated by the dotted pole in Fig. 32, the M.M.F. diagram in Fig. 33 remains unchanged, but the flux density no longer bears the same ratio to the M.M.F. at every point, and must be determined by resolving the armature M.M.F. into components $\mathbf{M}_d$ and $\mathbf{M}_q$ along the two axes. It is assumed that each component of M.M.F. produces a proportional flux along the same axis, but that the factor of proportionality is different for the two axes. The figure $OSLT$ of Fig. 36 is the modified voltage vector diagram based on this assumption.

The component vectors $\mathbf{M}_d$ and $\mathbf{M}_q$ in the space vector diagram of M.M.F.s (Fig. 33) correspond to component vectors $\mathbf{I}_d$ and $\mathbf{I}_q$ in the time vector diagram of currents (Fig. 36). The voltage induced by the direct-axis component of flux is represented by $LT$ in Fig. 36, and is equal to $jx_{md}\mathbf{I}_d$, where $x_{md}$ is the *direct-axis magnetising reactance*. Similarly the voltage induced by the quadrature-axis component of flux, represented by $SL$, is equal to $jx_{mq}\mathbf{I}_q$, where $x_{mq}$ is the *quadrature-axis magnetising reactance*. The open-circuit voltage $\mathbf{E}_0$, the internal voltage $\mathbf{E}_i$, the resistance and leakage reactance drops, and the terminal voltage $\mathbf{E}$ remain as before.

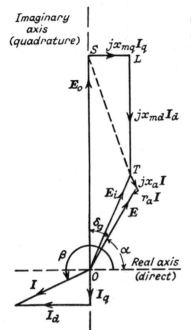

Fig. 36.—Vector diagram of a salient-pole synchronous machine.

The vector equation corresponding to the vector diagram of Fig. 36 is:

$$\mathbf{E}=\mathbf{E}_0+r_a\mathbf{I}+jx_d\mathbf{I}_d+jx_q\mathbf{I}_q, \qquad \dots(5.5)$$

where $x_d=x_{md}+x_a$ (direct-axis synchronous reactance),

$x_q=x_{mq}+x_a$ (quadrature-axis synchronous reactance).

Thus the two-axis vector diagram of the salient-pole machine is in itself little more complicated than the diagram of the cylindrical-rotor machine. It is, however, more difficult to apply, because the resolution of the current vector introduces the unknown angle $\beta$. It is not possible to derive a simple equivalent circuit for determining the current corresponding to a given supply voltage. An approximate method for determining the angle $\beta$ and other quantities is given in the next section.

The vector $\mathbf{I}_d$ is called the *direct-axis component* of the current, and $\mathbf{I}_q$ is called the *quadrature-axis component*, because they correspond to the components of the M.M.F. along the two axes. The words 'direct' and 'quadrature' are shown on Figs. 34 and 36 in brackets, because, although they are used for the current components, they apply strictly to the space vector diagram of M.M.F.s, and not to the time vector diagram of currents. The resolution of the current into the axis components corresponds to the transformation from phase values to axis values in the general theory. The process is, however, simpler than the general transformation, as it consists only of the resolution of a time vector. The question is discussed further in Sect. 28, where the steady-state theory, instead of being worked out from first principles, is derived as a special case of the general theory.

## 22. The Power-angle Characteristic of a Synchronous Machine

A synchronous machine normally operates in conjunction with an external supply system, and for many purposes the supply voltage may be considered as a fixed reference, both as regards magnitude and phase. If the machine of Fig. 32 is driven in such a way as to generate a fixed terminal voltage in phase $A$ when on open circuit, the position occupied by the rotor at any instant is determined by this voltage. Conversely, the voltage of an external supply system can be associated with a uniformly rotating reference axis, whose position is that which the axis of the rotor would have if it were driven in such a way as to generate the external voltage on open circuit. The position of the rotor during any operating condition can then be measured by its displacement relative to the reference axis.

When the synchronous machine is operating steadily on load, the speed is still the constant synchronous speed $\omega$, but the angular position is displaced from the reference position by a constant angle $\delta$. The angle $\delta$ is called the *load angle*, because its value varies progressively with the load, and it is taken as positive when the input power is positive; that is, when the machine operates as a motor. The curve relating the input power $P$ and the load angle $\delta$ is called the *power-angle characteristic*.

The value of $\delta$ is given by the angle between $\mathbf{E_0}$ and $\mathbf{E}$ in the vector diagram. The vector diagram (Fig. 36) is drawn so as to relate particularly to generator operation, when the value of $\delta$ is negative. Hence the angle between $\mathbf{E}$ and $\mathbf{E_0}$ is $\delta_g = -\delta$. Moreover the electrical input power $P$ is negative for generator operation, and the generator output is $P_g = -P$. The relation between $P_g$ and $\delta_g$ can be deduced from the diagram as a simple expression if the armature resistance $r_a$ is neglected.

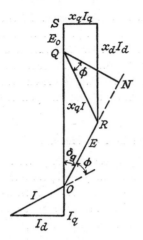

FIG. 37.—Simplified vector diagram of a synchronous machine.

Fig. 37 shows a simplified form of the vector diagram of Fig. 36 in which $r_a\mathbf{I}$ is omitted, and each component of magnetising reactance drop is combined with the corresponding component of the leakage reactance drop $jx_a\mathbf{I}$ to give a component of synchronous reactance drop. If the symbols $I$, $I_d$ and $I_q$ are used for the magnitudes of the vectors representing the currents, the magnitudes of the direct and quadrature-axis components of synchronous reactance drop are $x_dI_d$ and $x_qI_q$. Thus Fig. 37 agrees with Eqn. (5.5) if the resistance drop is omitted. The generator load angle $\delta_g$ and the power factor angle $\varphi$ are indicated on the diagram.

The end of the voltage vector $\mathbf{E}$ is designated $R$. In order to determine $\delta_g$, a line $RQ$ is drawn perpendicular to the current vector, meeting $OS$ in $Q$, and a perpendicular $QN$ is dropped on $OR$ produced. The angle $RQN = \varphi$, and

$$RQ = \frac{x_qI_q}{\sin OQR} = x_qI.$$

Hence

$$\tan \delta_g = \frac{NQ}{ON} = \frac{x_qI \cos \varphi}{E + x_qI \sin \varphi}. \qquad \text{...(5.6)}$$

Also

$$\left.\begin{aligned}
I \cos \varphi &= I_d \sin \delta_g + I_q \cos \delta_g\\
I \sin \varphi &= I_d \cos \delta_g - I_q \sin \delta_g\\
E_0 - E \cos \delta_g &= I_d x_d\\
E \sin \delta_g &= I_q x_q
\end{aligned}\right\} \qquad \text{...(5.7)}$$

For a three-phase generator, unit power is defined as the total power in all three phases, corresponding to unit R.M.S. voltage and unit R.M.S. current at unity power factor in each phase. Hence the generator output power is given by:

$$P_g = EI \cos \varphi,$$

98

which can be written, using Eqns. (5.7),

$$P_g = \left[ \frac{EE_0}{x_d} \sin \delta_g + \frac{E^2}{2} \left( \frac{1}{x_q} - \frac{1}{x_d} \right) \sin 2\delta_g \right]. \qquad \dots(5.8)$$

The full-line curve in Fig. 38 shows the power-angle characteristic obtained by plotting $P_g$ against $\delta_g$ for a salient-pole machine. For a cylindrical-rotor machine, with $x_d = x_q$, the second term in Eqn. (5.8) is zero, and the curve becomes simply the sine curve shown by the dotted line.

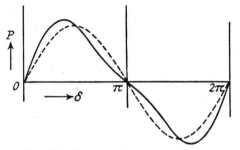

FIG. 38.—Power-angle characteristic of a
synchronous machine.

If this result is given in terms of the motoring load angle $\delta$ and the input power $P$, the form of the equation is the same. With unit torque defined as the torque that develops unit power at speed $\omega$, and with all losses neglected, the motoring torque $F_m$ at speed $\omega$ is given by the same formula:

$$F_m = P = \left[ \frac{EE_0}{x_d} \sin \delta + \frac{E^2}{2} \left( \frac{1}{x_q} - \frac{1}{x_d} \right) \sin 2\delta \right]. \qquad \dots(5.9)$$

*Synchronising torque coefficient*

Since the torque of a synchronous machine, with fixed terminal voltage and field current, increases with the load angle, the machine is equivalent to a torsional spring connected between the output shaft and the rotating reference axis which depends on the supply voltage, as explained on page 97. If the rotor lags behind the reference axis, $\delta$ is positive, and the machine acts as a motor, developing a motoring torque which tends to accelerate the rotor. When the rotor runs ahead of the reference axis, the machine is a generator and causes the opposite effect.

At small angles, whether positive or negative, the torque is approximately proportional to the displacement, but as the angle increases, the torque increases less rapidly and eventually reaches a maximum. Thus the spring, to which the machine is equivalent, has a non-linear characteristic. The effective spring constant for small changes relative to any steady condition is given by the slope of the curve. It is called the *synchronising torque coefficient*, and is denoted by $P_0$. Its value is:

$$P_0 = \frac{dP}{d\delta} = \left[ \frac{EE_0}{x_d} \cos \delta + E^2 \left( \frac{1}{x_q} - \frac{1}{x_d} \right) \cos 2\delta \right]. \quad \ldots (5.10)$$

It should be noted that the effective spring constant, deduced from the steady-state characteristic, is only correct for slow changes. When rapid changes occur the conditions may be greatly modified by the action of the field and damper windings, as shown in Sect. 38.

# CHAPTER VI

# General Equations for A.C. Machines

## 23. Transformation Formulae for a Rotating Three-phase Winding

The idealised synchronous machine represented by the two-pole diagram of Fig. 3 has a rotating three-phase winding. It is possible to set up a voltage equation for each coil of such a machine by adding the component voltages due to all the currents, but some of the coefficients in the equations so obtained are variable. The variable coefficients are the self- and mutual inductances of the armature coils or the mutual inductances between armature and stator coils, and they vary with $\theta$, the angle defining the position of the armature at any instant. The equations are therefore difficult to solve. The equations of A.C. machines are obtained in a simpler form, first suggested by Park, if the variables for the armature winding are not the actual phase voltages and currents $e_a$, $e_b$, $e_c$, $i_a$, $i_b$, $i_c$, but are new fictitious quantities $e_d$, $e_q$, $e_0$, $i_d$, $i_q$, $i_0$, which differ from, but are related to, the actual quantities. The process of replacing one set of variables by another related set is known as a *transformation*, as explained on page 14. The method of analysis of A.C. machines expressed by the transformed equations is termed the *two-axis theory*.

In the first instance the transformation may be regarded as a mathematical process, but it is also possible to assign a physical meaning to the new quantities. For reasons which appear in the following pages, $e_d$, $e_q$, $i_d$, $i_q$, are associated with fictitious coils located on the direct and quadrature axes, like those marked $D$ and $Q$ in Fig. 5, and are called *axis voltages and currents*, and $e_0$, $i_0$ are called the *zero-sequence voltage and current*.

*The direct and quadrature axis currents*

The axis currents $i_d$ and $i_q$ are defined as the currents in fictitious coils, located on the axes and each having the same number of turns as a phase coil, which would set up the same M.M.F. wave as the actual currents $i_a$, $i_b$, $i_c$. Because of the fact that the three actual coils are replaced by a system of two axis coils, it is advantageous, in order to retain the definition of unit power for an A.C. machine given on page 32, to change the unit of current in the axis coils to a value one and a half times the unit for the phase coils.

The maximum of the sinusoidal M.M.F. wave due to the current $i_a$ in the phase coil $A$ of Fig. 3 is proportional to $i_a$ and occurs at the axis of the coil; that is, at the angular position $\theta$. The M.M.F. wave due to $i_a$ may be resolved into two components, one along each of the direct and quadrature axes. The amplitude of the direct-axis component is:

$$k_m i_a \cos \theta,$$

where $k_m$ is a constant.

The direct-axis component of the resultant M.M.F. wave, due to the combined action of the three-phase currents, is therefore of amplitude

$$k_m \left\{ i_a \cos \theta + i_b \cos \left( \theta - \frac{2\pi}{3} \right) + i_c \cos \left( \theta - \frac{4\pi}{3} \right) \right\}.$$

The amplitude of the M.M.F. wave due to the current $i_d$ in the direct-axis coil, taking into account the change of unit explained above, is

$$\tfrac{3}{2} k_m i_d.$$

Hence $i_d$ is given by:

$$i_d = \frac{2}{3} \left[ i_a \cos \theta + i_b \cos \left( \theta - \frac{2\pi}{3} \right) + i_c \cos \left( \theta - \frac{4\pi}{3} \right) \right].$$

Similarly the quadrature-axis current $i_q$ is given by:

$$i_q = \frac{2}{3} \left[ i_a \sin \theta + i_b \sin \left( \theta - \frac{2\pi}{3} \right) + i_c \sin \left( \theta - \frac{4\pi}{3} \right) \right].$$

*The zero-sequence current*

The current $i_0$ is defined by:

$$i_0 = \tfrac{1}{3}(i_a + i_b + i_c).$$

The term 'zero-sequence current' is adopted from the analogy with the 'zero-sequence component' used in symmetrical component theory, but $i_0$ is an instantaneous value of current, which may vary with time in any manner. It may be visualised physically as the magnitude of each of a set of equal currents, flowing in all three phases and therefore producing no resultant air-gap M.M.F.

## The current transformations

The transformation equations giving the new currents in terms of the actual currents are therefore expressed by the following matrix equations:

$$
\begin{vmatrix} i_d \\ i_q \\ i_0 \end{vmatrix} = \frac{2}{3} \begin{vmatrix} \cos\theta & \cos\left(\theta - \dfrac{2\pi}{3}\right) & \cos\left(\theta - \dfrac{4\pi}{3}\right) \\ \sin\theta & \sin\left(\theta - \dfrac{2\pi}{3}\right) & \sin\left(\theta - \dfrac{4\pi}{3}\right) \\ \dfrac{1}{2} & \dfrac{1}{2} & \dfrac{1}{2} \end{vmatrix} \cdot \begin{vmatrix} i_a \\ i_b \\ i_c \end{vmatrix} \quad \dots(6.1)
$$

The equations of the *inverse transformation*, giving the actual currents $i_a$, $i_b$, $i_c$, in terms of the new currents $i_d$, $i_q$, $i_0$, are obtained by solving the above equations.

$$
\begin{vmatrix} i_a \\ i_b \\ i_c \end{vmatrix} = \begin{vmatrix} \cos\theta & \sin\theta & 1 \\ \cos\left(\theta - \dfrac{2\pi}{3}\right) & \sin\left(\theta - \dfrac{2\pi}{3}\right) & 1 \\ \cos\left(\theta - \dfrac{4\pi}{3}\right) & \sin\left(\theta - \dfrac{4\pi}{3}\right) & 1 \end{vmatrix} \cdot \begin{vmatrix} i_d \\ i_q \\ i_0 \end{vmatrix} \quad \dots(6.2)
$$

It may be noted that, because of the rather arbitrary choice of unit, Eqns. (6.1) contain a numerical factor, but the inverse transformation equations (6.2) do not. It is shown later on page 107 that, as a result of this choice of current unit, the circuit equations (6.7) relating the axis quantities are obtained in a form which does not introduce a numerical factor.

### The voltage transformations

The new voltages are defined by a set of equations exactly similar to those for the currents.

$$
\begin{vmatrix} e_d \\ e_q \\ e_0 \end{vmatrix} = \frac{2}{3}
\begin{vmatrix}
\cos\theta & \cos\left(\theta - \dfrac{2\pi}{3}\right) & \cos\left(\theta - \dfrac{4\pi}{3}\right) \\
\sin\theta & \sin\left(\theta - \dfrac{2\pi}{3}\right) & \sin\left(\theta - \dfrac{4\pi}{3}\right) \\
\dfrac{1}{2} & \dfrac{1}{2} & \dfrac{1}{2}
\end{vmatrix}
\cdot
\begin{vmatrix} e_a \\ e_b \\ e_c \end{vmatrix}
\qquad \ldots(6.3)
$$

The equations of the inverse transformation are:

$$
\begin{vmatrix} e_a \\ e_b \\ e_c \end{vmatrix} =
\begin{vmatrix}
\cos\theta & \sin\theta & 1 \\
\cos\left(\theta - \dfrac{2\pi}{3}\right) & \sin\left(\theta - \dfrac{2\pi}{3}\right) & 1 \\
\cos\left(\theta - \dfrac{4\pi}{3}\right) & \sin\left(\theta - \dfrac{4\pi}{3}\right) & 1
\end{vmatrix}
\cdot
\begin{vmatrix} e_d \\ e_q \\ e_0 \end{vmatrix}
\qquad \ldots(6.4)
$$

### Power input

Using the definition of unit power given on page 32, the power input to a three-phase armature winding is given by:

$$P = \tfrac{1}{3}(e_a i_a + e_b i_b + e_c i_c). \qquad \ldots(6.5)$$

By substituting the expressions for the currents and voltages given by the transformation equations (6.2) and (6.4) it can readily be shown that:

$$P = \tfrac{1}{2}(e_d i_d + e_q i_q) + e_0 i_0. \qquad \ldots(6.6)$$

For normal steady operation with balanced polyphase voltages and currents the quantities $e_0$ and $i_0$ are zero. Hence Eqn. (6.6) accords with the definition of unit power for a machine with two main circuits.

*Distribution of the armature winding*

It has been assumed that the M.M.F. wave due to a current in an armature coil is sinusoidal. In fact, harmonic M.M.F. waves are also set up, but they are neglected in the theory. The value of any harmonic M.M.F. wave depends on a harmonic winding factor, which can be calculated for any manner of distribution of the conductors. The assumption that all the harmonic winding factors are negligible is explained in Park's definition by stating that the winding is 'sinusoidally distributed'.

The harmonic winding factors also determine the voltages induced in a winding by harmonic fluxes. In a salient-pole machine the curve of flux density distribution in the air-gap may depart considerably from a sine wave even if the M.M.F. wave producing it is sinusoidal. Nevertheless, because the harmonic winding factors are negligible, it is only the fundamental component of the flux wave that needs to be considered when calculating the armature voltages.

*Flux linkage*

The unit of flux in the per-unit system is defined on page 18 for a transformer to be such that unit rate of change of flux induces unit voltage in any coil. For a machine the definition must be amplified by the stipulation that the axis of the flux wave is coincident with the axis of the coil in which the voltage is induced. For this condition the flux becomes identical with the 'flux linkage' with the coil. In the theory that follows the flux linkage is denoted by the symbol $\psi$ and is used as a measure of the flux.

At any instant the flux wave existing in the air-gap requires a magnitude and an angle to define it completely. It may therefore be expressed by the flux linkage $\psi_m$ with a coil having the same axis, together with an angle giving the angular position of the axis. Alternatively the flux wave may be resolved into two components on the direct and quadrature axes, and

105

expressed by the corresponding direct and quadrature axis flux linkages $\psi_{md}$ and $\psi_{mq}$. In practice the resolution into axis components proves to be the best method of expressing the instantaneous value of the flux.

Following Park's terminology, each of the flux linkages $\psi_{md}$ and $\psi_{mq}$ used to express the air-gap flux is understood to be the flux linkage with a coil on the corresponding axis. Subject to this condition, they represent the flux linkage with any of the various coils whatever the actual number of turns, because of the way in which the unit of voltage in any secondary winding is defined, as explained on page 18.

### The induced voltage in the armature

Assuming that the component flux linkages $\psi_{md}$ and $\psi_{mq}$ are known, the induced voltage in an armature coil can be determined and a voltage equation for the circuit can be derived. The voltage induced in coil $A$ depends on its angular position $\theta$ as well as on the flux linkage components, since the voltage induced in a coil is reduced when the axis of the coil is displaced from the axis of the flux. The voltage induced by $\psi_{md}$ is $-p(\psi_{md} \cos \theta)$ and that due to $\psi_{mq}$ is $-p(\psi_{mq} \sin \theta)$. Hence the total internal voltage, opposing the voltage induced by the main air-gap flux, is:

$$p(\psi_{md} \cos \theta + \psi_{mq} \sin \theta).$$

Now the air-gap flux is produced by the combined action of the currents in all the windings on the stator and rotor. The armature currents, however, also produce local fluxes which do not cross the air-gap but which nevertheless link phase $A$. The current $i_a$ produces a leakage reactance drop $l_1 p i_a$, where $l_1$ is the leakage inductance of coil $A$. Currents $i_b$ and $i_c$ produce drops $-l_m p i_b$ and $-l_m p i_c$ in coil $A$, where $l_m$ is the part of the mutual inductance between two armature coils due to flux which does not cross the air-gap. The terms have negative signs because the coils are displaced from each other by 120°. To a good approximation the inductances $l_1$ and $l_m$ are independent of rotor position.

The impressed voltage $e_a$ is equal to the sum of the internal voltage due to the main air-gap flux, the drops due to the local armature fluxes, and the resistance drop $r_a i_a$. Hence the equation is:

$$e_a = p(\psi_{md} \cos \theta + \psi_{mq} \sin \theta) + (r_a + l_1 p) i_a - l_m p i_b - l_m p i_c.$$

Using the relation $i_a + i_b + i_c = 3 i_0$, and the value of $i_a$ given by Eqns. (6.2), the equation becomes:

$$
\begin{aligned}
e_a &= p[\psi_{md} \cos \theta + \psi_{mq} \sin \theta] \\
&\quad + (l_1 + l_m) p(i_d \cos \theta + i_q \sin \theta + i_0) - 3 l_m p i_0 + r_a i_a \\
&= p[(\psi_{md} + l_a i_d) \cos \theta + (\psi_{mq} + l_a i_q) \sin \theta] + l_0 p i_0 + r_a i_a \\
&= p[\psi_d \cos \theta + \psi_q \sin \theta] + l_0 p i_0 + r_a i_a,
\end{aligned}
$$

where the following new quantities are introduced:

$$
\begin{aligned}
l_a &= l_1 + l_m, \\
l_0 &= l_a - 3 l_m, \\
\psi_d &= \psi_{md} + l_a i_d, \\
\psi_q &= \psi_{mq} + l_a i_q.
\end{aligned}
$$

The quantities $\psi_d$ and $\psi_q$ are the total flux linkages with an armature coil located on the appropriate axis, due to both the main air-gap flux and the armature leakage flux; $l_a$ is the 'effective' leakage inductance of either of the axis coils. The inductance $l_0$ associated with the zero-sequence current is the *zero-sequence inductance*, which is a well-known quantity in symmetrical component theory.

Equations for the voltages $e_d$, $e_q$, $e_0$ may now be found by expanding and rearranging the above equation, using the values of $i_a$ and $e_a$ from the transformation equations (6.2) and (6.4), and differentiating the product terms in the square bracket, putting $p\theta = v$. Then:

$$
\begin{aligned}
(e_d - r_a i_d) \cos \theta + (e_q - r_a i_q) \sin \theta &+ (e_0 - r_a i_0 - l_0 p i_0) \\
&= \cos \theta \, (p\psi_d + v\psi_q) + \sin \theta (p\psi_q - v\psi_d).
\end{aligned}
$$

This equation must hold for all values of $\theta$ and it therefore follows by equating coefficients that:

$$
\left.
\begin{aligned}
e_d &= p\psi_d + v\psi_q + r_a i_d \\
e_q &= -v\psi_d + p\psi_q + r_a i_q \\
e_0 &= (r_a + l_0 p) i_0
\end{aligned}
\right\} \qquad \ldots (6.7)
$$

The method of equating coefficients, which is used frequently throughout the book, provides an elegant method of obtaining the above result. The method is a rigorous one, but any reader who is not satisfied about its validity should work through the rather lengthy process of obtaining expressions for $e_a$, $e_b$ and $e_c$, and substituting in the transformation equations (6.3) to obtain $e_d$, $e_q$ and $e_0$. It would lead to the same result.

Eqns. (6.7) form the basis of the two-axis theory. The quantities $e_0$ and $i_0$ are related to each other independently of the others, and for many problems only the axis voltages and currents need to be considered. Thus the transformation brings about a great simplification.

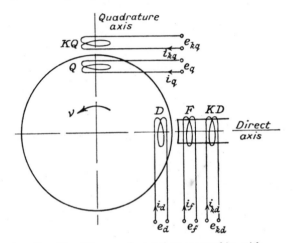

FIG. 39.—Diagram of a synchronous machine with two damper coils.

## The fictitious axis coils in the generalised machine

The two equations for the axis quantities are identical with Eqns. (3.5) for the D.C. machine. It follows that, for the A.C. machine, the voltages $e_d$ and $e_q$, which were defined arbitrarily by Eqns. (6.3), can be interpreted as the impressed voltages on the direct and quadrature axis coils, provided that these coils possess the pseudo-stationary property defined on page 15. The synchronous machine of Fig. 3 can then be replaced by the generalised machine of Fig. 39, in which the coils $D$ and $Q$ are pseudo-stationary coils located on the axes. Thus the same generalised machine diagram applies to both the D.C. machine

108

and the A.C. machine. As with the D.C. machine the terms in Eqns. (6.7) containing $p$ are called transformer voltages and those containing $\nu$ are called rotation voltages.

The form of the armature voltage equations leads to a simple method of writing down the complete equations of a synchronous machine. If the coils $D$ and $Q$ of Fig. 39 were ordinary stationary coils the voltage equations would be:

$$e_d = p\psi_d + r_a i_d,$$
$$e_q = p\psi_q + r_a i_q.$$

Eqns. (6.7) differ from these equations only by the presence of the rotation voltage terms. The complete equations for the machine of Fig. 39 can therefore be derived by first writing down the five equations for a set of five stationary coils, and then adding to the two armature equations additional terms for the rotation voltages. The method is used in the following two sections.

*The torque equation*

It is shown on page 34 that the electrical torque developed by a machine, which has two armature coils $D$ and $Q$ on the direct and quadrature axes as in Fig. 5, may be determined from the rotation voltage terms in the armature equations. It has also been shown on page 104 that, in order to calculate the power passing into the axis coils, the factor $k_p$ must have the value $\frac{1}{2}$. The expression for the total input power $P$ contains, in addition to those included in Eqn. (2.5), the term

$$e_0 i_0 = r_a i_0{}^2 + l_0 i_0 \frac{di_0}{dt}.$$

This power is, however, entirely absorbed as ohmic loss or as stored magnetic energy, and hence, following the argument explained on page 34, contributes nothing to the torque.

From the rotation voltage terms in Eqns. (6.7), the output power is therefore:

$$P_e = \frac{\nu}{2}(\psi_q i_d - \psi_d i_q).$$

Hence the torque equation is:

$$f_e = \frac{\omega}{2}(\psi_d i_q - \psi_q i_d). \qquad \ldots(6.8)$$

The expression for the torque shows the two components of torque discussed on page 30. The first component is due to the interaction between the direct-axis flux and the quadrature-axis current and has a positive sign. The second component is due to the interaction between the quadrature-axis flux and the direct-axis current and has a negative sign. No torque is produced by interaction between flux and current on the same axis.

### 24. General Equations of the Synchronous Machine

*Field and damper windings*

The field winding of a synchronous machine consists of coils round the poles and forms a single circuit. In the diagram of

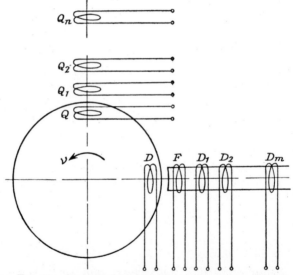

Fig. 40.—Generalised diagram of a synchronous machine.

the idealised two-pole machine it is represented by a single coil $F$ on the direct axis, as in Fig. 39 or 40. Under normal conditions the impressed voltage $e_f$ is supplied from an exciter or other D.C. source.

110

The damper winding accounts for all the other closed circuits on the field system. The commonest form of damper winding consists of squirrel-cage bars in the pole face connected together at the ends by rings or segments. Sometimes a field collar, provided as a support for the field winding, forms a closed circuit round the pole. There are also eddy current paths in the iron, whether solid or laminated, of the magnet system. All

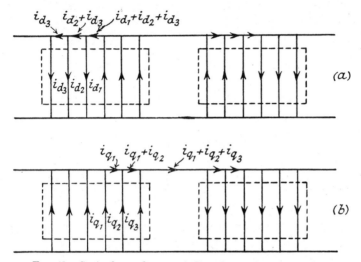

FIG. 41.—Squirrel-cage damper winding of a synchronous machine.

these circuits react to changes in the flux of the machine, and for a complete representation in the idealised machine a large number of circuits is necessary. Normally no external voltages are impressed on the damper circuits.

All the damper circuits are normally symmetrical with respect to both the direct and quadrature axes and can be represented in the diagram (Fig. 40) by $m$ direct-axis coils and $n$ quadrature axis coils. The coils representing the squirrel-cage bars or eddy current paths are interconnected at the ends of the core as explained in the next paragraph. The eddy current paths in the iron can be considered as a squirrel cage having an infinite number of bars, and require an infinite number of damper coils for their representation. For practical work only an

111

approximate representation, using a small number of damper coils, is feasible.

Consider a squirrel-cage winding of the type represented in Fig. 41, in which there are six bars in the pole face (shown dotted) connected by complete end rings. Such a winding requires three direct-axis coils and three quadrature-axis coils in the idealised machine. Fig. 41(a) shows the paths of the direct-axis currents and Fig. 41(b) those of the quadrature-axis currents. In the actual machine the currents $i_{d1}$, $i_{d2}$, $i_{d3}$, $i_{q1}$, $i_{q2}$, $i_{q3}$, are superimposed in the bars and rings. Because of the symmetry about the axes there is no mutual action between the direct and quadrature axis coils, but there is a mutual inductive coupling between the three coils of one axis. There is also a mutual resistance coupling because the current in any pair of bars flows through the end rings and introduces an ohmic drop in the circuit through any other pair of bars.

The majority of damper windings in synchronous machines have a simplified construction in which the parts of the end-rings between the poles are omitted. There are, however, always paths through the iron which complete the quadrature circuits. Similarly the eddy current paths in the iron of a solid pole machine can be represented approximately by an appropriate number of damper circuits on the two axes.

*Direct-axis equations*

The equations for a system of stationary mutually coupled coils comprising coils $D$, $F$ and $D1$ to $D_m$ of Fig. 40 can be written down in terms of their self- and mutual operational impedances. For the rotating machine, however, the equation for the armature coil $D$ is the first of Eqns. (6.7), and differs from that for a stationary coil because of the rotation voltage term $\nu\psi_q$.

The flux linkage $\psi_d$ depends only on the direct-axis currents and is given by:

$$\psi_d = M_f i_f + M_{d1} i_{d1} + M_{d2} i_{d2} + \ldots + L_d i_d, \qquad \ldots(6.9)$$

where $M_f$, $M_{d1}$, etc., are the mutual inductances between coils $F$, $D1$, etc., and coil $D$, and $L_d$ is the complete self-inductance of coil $D$.

The equations for the field and direct-axis damper coils are as follows:

$$
\left.
\begin{aligned}
e_f &= (r_f + L_f p)i_f + M_{fd1}pi_{d1} + M_{fd2}pi_{d2} + \ldots + M_f pi_a \\
0 &= M_{fd1}pi_f + (r_{d1} + L_{d1}p)i_{d1} + (r_{d12} + M_{d12}p)i_{d2} \\
&\qquad\qquad + \ldots + M_{d1}pi_a \\
0 &= M_{fd2}pi_f + (r_{d12} + M_{d12}p)i_{d1} + (r_{d2} + L_{d2}p)i_{d2} \\
&\qquad\qquad + \ldots + M_{d2}pi_a
\end{aligned}
\right\} \ldots (6.10)
$$

etc.

where $r_f$, $r_{d1}$, $r_{d2}$, $L_f$, $L_{d1}$, $L_{d2}$, etc., are the resistances and complete self-inductances of the coils $F$, $D1$, $D2$, etc. $M_{fd1}$ is the mutual inductance between coils $F$ and $D1$, $M_{d12}$ is the mutual inductance between coils $D1$ and $D2$, $r_{d12}$ is the mutual resistance between coils $D1$ and $D2$,

and similarly for other pairs of coils.

Eqns. (6.9) and (6.10) form a set of $(m+2)$ equations containing $(m+2)$ currents, as well as the quantities $e_f$ and $\psi_d$. In many problems the currents in the field and damper windings are not required and may be eliminated from the equations, giving a single operational relation between $\psi_d$, $i_d$ and $e_f$ of the form:

$$
\psi_d = \frac{x_d(p)}{\omega} i_d + \frac{G(p)}{\omega} e_f. \qquad \ldots (6.11)
$$

The factor $\omega$ in the denominator of Eqn. (6.11) is introduced in order that $x_d(p)$ shall have the dimensions of an operational impedance.

The elimination is best carried out by means of determinants. $x_d(p)$ and $G(p)$ are functions of $p$, obtained in each case as the quotient of two determinants, each of which, when worked out, is a polynomial expression in $p$. $x_d(p)$ is an algebraic expression of the form:

$$
x_d(p) = \frac{b_{(m+1)}p^{m+1} + b_m p^m + \ldots + b_0}{a_{(m+1)}p^{m+1} + a_m p^m + \ldots + a_0},
$$

in which both numerator and denominator are of order $(m+1)$. $G(p)$ has the same denominator as $x_d(p)$ but a different numerator of order $m$.

*Quadrature-axis equations*

The quadrature-axis equations are similar to those for the direct axis, but are simpler because there is no quadrature field winding. The symbols used correspond to those in the direct-axis equations:

$$\psi_q = M_{q1}i_{q1} + M_{q2}i_{q2} + \ldots + L_q i_q, \qquad \ldots(6.12)$$

$$\left. \begin{aligned} 0 &= (r_{q1} + L_{q1}p)i_{q1} + (r_{q12} + M_{q12}p)i_{q2} + \ldots + M_{q1}pi_q \\ 0 &= (r_{q12} + M_{q12}p)i_{q1} + (r_{q2} + L_{q2}p)i_{q2} + \ldots + M_{q2}pi_q \\ &\quad \text{etc.} \end{aligned} \right\}, \qquad \ldots(6.13)$$

Elimination of the damper currents from the set of $(n+1)$ equations gives:

$$\psi_q = \frac{x_q(p)}{\omega} i_q, \qquad \ldots(6.14)$$

where $x_q(p)$ is a function of $p$ which is the quotient of two polynomials of order $n$.

*Complete equations and equivalent circuits*

The complete equations of the synchronous machine can thus be reduced to the equations (6.7), (6.8), (6.11) and (6.14). If the zero-sequence equation is omitted there are five equations, which are collected together on page 121. 

The principal complication in applying the equations to practical problems arises in handling the operational expressions $x_d(p)$, $x_q(p)$ and $G(p)$. For some purposes it is more convenient to derive these quantities from equivalent networks rather than by solving the equations. The equivalent networks are particularly helpful in dealing with steady A.C. problems, when the solution may be obtained by means of a network analyser.

Considering first the direct axis, if Eqn. (6.9) is multiplied by $p$, $p\psi_d$ can be treated as an applied voltage. For a set of linear equations like Eqns. (6.9) and (6.10), in which all the mutual coefficients are equal in pairs, it is always possible to find a network to which the equations apply. $p\psi_d$ is the main applied voltage and $e_f$ appears as an impressed voltage in a branch of the network which corresponds to the field circuit. Similarly another equivalent network can be found for the quadrature axis, with $p\psi_q$ as the main applied voltage.

In this book the equivalent networks are only given for the simplified machine treated in the next section. The simplified machine, represented by Fig. 39, provides the best means of explaining the nature of the equivalent circuits, and it suffices for many practical problems. For a detailed treatment of the general equivalent circuits of the synchronous machine the reader is referred to Ref. 45.2.

### 25. Simplified Equations of a Synchronous Machine with Two Damper Coils

For all the synchronous machine problems studied in the next few chapters the equations used are those of a simplified machine with one damper coil $KD$ on the direct axis and one damper coil $KQ$ on the quadrature axis, as in Fig. 39. Although it is only an approximation the results obtained are accurate enough for most purposes; for example, the concept of transient and subtransient reactances depends on this simplification. Even on this basis the working out of a practical solution is quite complicated enough, and it is often necessary to introduce still further approximations. On the other hand, the general equations of the last section provide the means of making a more detailed study if the discrepancies are too great; for example, in machines with solid poles or complicated damping systems.

For the simplified machine Eqns. (6.9) and (6.10) now reduce to three direct-axis equations:

$$\left.\begin{array}{l} \psi_d = M_f i_f + M_{kd} i_{kd} + L_d i_d \\ e_f = (r_f + L_f p) i_f + M_{fkd} p i_{kd} + M_f p i_d \\ 0 = M_{fkd} p i_f + (r_{kd} + L_{kd} p) i_{kd} + M_{kd} p i_d \end{array}\right\}. \qquad (6.15)$$

Similarly Eqns. (6.12) and (6.13) reduce to two quadrature axis equations:

$$\left.\begin{array}{l} \psi_q = M_{kq} i_{kq} + L_q i_q \\ 0 = (r_{kq} + L_{kq} p) i_{kq} + M_{kq} p i_q \end{array}\right\}. \qquad (6.16)$$

115

The functions $x_d(p)$, $G(p)$ and $x_q(p)$ of Eqns. (6.11) and (6.14) are very much simpler than before and are of the form:

$$x_d(p) = \frac{b_2 p^2 + b_1 p + b_0}{a_2 p^2 + a_1 p + a_0},$$

$$G(p) = \frac{g_1 p + g_0}{a_2 p^2 + a_1 p + a_0},$$

$$x_q(p) = \frac{d_1 p + d_0}{c_1 p + c_0}.$$

*Equations using per-unit leakage inductances*

Eqns. (6.9) to (6.16) hold whether the stator quantities are on a per-unit basis or not. They become easier to handle, however, if per-unit quantities are used (see page 19), and if, in addition, it is assumed that the three per-unit mutual inductances on the direct axis are all equal. The assumption is very nearly true for a normal synchronous machine, because the leakage fluxes of the field coils and the damper bars are distinct and there is a single main flux linking them and the armature winding. In special cases—for example, a machine with short-circuited field collars at the bottom of the poles—the more exact equations must be used.

On a per-unit basis, with the above assumption:

$$M_{kd} = M_f = M_{fkd} = L_{md},$$
$$M_{kq} = L_{mq},$$

where $L_{md}$, $L_{mq}$ are the per-unit mutual inductances, or *magnetising inductances*, on the two axes.

The complete self-inductance of each coil is the sum of the mutual inductance and the leakage inductance (see page 19). Hence:

$$L_d = L_{md} + l_a,$$
$$L_f = L_{md} + l_f,$$
$$L_{kd} = L_{md} + l_{kd},$$
$$L_q = L_{mq} + l_a,$$
$$L_{kq} = L_{mq} + l_{kq},$$

where $l_a$, $l_f$, $l_{kd}$, $l_{kq}$ are per-unit leakage inductances. The armature leakage inductance $l_a$ is the quantity determined on page 107 and is assumed to have the same value for both axes.

Eqns. (6.15) and (6.16) now become:

$$\left.\begin{array}{l} \psi_d = L_{md}i_f + L_{md}i_{kd} + (L_{md} + l_a)i_d \\ e_f = \{r_f + (L_{md} + l_f)p\}i_f + L_{md}pi_{kd} + L_{md}pi_d \\ 0 = L_{md}pi_f + \{r_{kd} + (L_{md} + l_{kd})p\}i_{kd} + L_{md}pi_d \end{array}\right\}, \dots (6.17)$$

$$\left.\begin{array}{l} \psi_q = L_{mq}i_{kq} + (L_{mq} + l_a)i_q \\ 0 = \{r_{kq} + (L_{mq} + l_{kq})p\}i_{kq} + L_{mq}pi_q \end{array}\right\}. \quad \dots (6.18)$$

Substitution of $\psi_d$ and $\psi_q$ in Eqns. (6.7) leads to the following set of five equations for the synchronous machine. For the sake of generality, impressed voltages $e_{kd}$ and $e_{kq}$ are shown for the damper circuits, although in practice they are almost always zero.

| | | | | | | | |
|---|---|---|---|---|---|---|---|
| $e_f$ | $=$ | $r_f + (L_{md} + l_f)p$ | $L_{md}p$ | | $L_{md}p$ | | $\cdot$ | $i_f$ |
| $e_{kd}$ | | $L_{md}p$ | $r_{kd} + (L_{md} + l_{kd})p$ | | $L_{md}p$ | | | $i_{kd}$ |
| $e_{kq}$ | | | | $r_{kq} + (L_{mq} + l_{kq})p$ | | $L_{mq}p$ | | $i_{ku}$ |
| $e_d$ | | $L_{md}p$ | $L_{md}p$ | $L_{mq}v$ | $r_a + (L_{md} + l_a)p$ | $(L_{mq} + l_a)v$ | | $i_d$ |
| $e_q$ | | $-L_{md}v$ | $-L_{md}v$ | $L_{mq}p$ | $- (L_{md} + l_a)v$ | $r_a + (L_{mq} + l_a)p$ | | $i_q$ |

$$\dots (6.19)$$

It should be noted that the equations do not introduce any special assumptions about the distribution of the stationary windings, except that they are symmetrical about the axis. The flux distribution in a synchronous machine, particularly one with salient poles, is not necessarily sinusoidal, and the values of self- and mutual inductance must allow for this. For the armature winding, however, the special assumption has been made that the harmonic winding factors are zero or negligible, as explained on page 105, so that an armature current produces no harmonic M.M.F. and no voltage is induced in the armature winding by a harmonic flux.

It was explained on page 25 that the effective number of turns of a distributed winding is not definite, and hence that the distinction between main flux and leakage flux is arbitrary, unless some assumption is made about the distribution of the flux. In the theory developed above, however, the magnetising inductances $L_{md}$ and $L_{mq}$ are based on the assumption of a sinusoidal air-gap flux wave, and the ratios of effective turns, on which the units for the stator windings depend, are thereby fixed. Thus there is no ambiguity about the division between magnetising inductance and leakage inductance.

*Equivalent circuits*

Fig. 42 shows two equivalent circuits, one for each axis, which can be used to assist in the analysis of the synchronous machine of Fig. 39. It is evident that the quantities in the

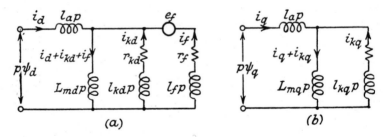

(a)                                        (b)

FIG. 42.—Equivalent circuits of a synchronous machine.
(a) Direct axis.                    (b) Quadrature axis.

network (Fig. 42(a)) satisfy Eqns. (6.17) and that the quantities in the network (Fig. 42(b)) satisfy Eqns. (6.18). These equivalent circuits, in which the elements are operational impedances, provide a convenient method of stating the relationships, and are often of assistance in obtaining numerical results. For the synchronous machine of Fig. 40, in which there are two or more damper circuits on each axis, similar equivalent circuits with more branches can be derived, as mentioned on page 114.

The equivalent circuits are of particular value for A.C. problems, for which the numerical results can be obtained either by calculation or with the aid of a network analyser. For transient problems, the equivalent circuits may be useful in devising suitable simulating equipment.

*The operational impedances $x_d(p)$ and $x_q(p)$ and the function $G(p)$*

By eliminating $i_f$ and $i_{kd}$ from Eqns. (6.17), $\psi_d$ may be expressed in the form of Eqn. (6.11). The value of $i_d$ is given by the quotient of two determinants as follows:

$$i_d = \frac{D_1}{D_2},$$

where

$$D_1 = \begin{vmatrix} e_f & r_f + (L_{md} + l_f)p & L_{md}p \\ 0 & L_{md}p & r_{kd} + (L_{md} + l_{kd})p \\ \psi_d & L_{md} & L_{md} \end{vmatrix}$$

$$= r_f r_{kd}[1 + (T_1 + T_2)p + T_1 T_3 p^2]\psi_d - L_{md}r_{kd}(1 + T_{kd}p)e_f,$$

$$D_2 = \begin{vmatrix} r_f + (L_{md} + l_f)p & L_{md}p & L_{md}p \\ L_{md}p & r_{kd} + (L_{md} + l_{kd})p & L_{md}p \\ L_{md} & L_{md} & L_{md} + l_a \end{vmatrix}$$

$$= r_f r_{kd} L_d[1 + (T_4 + T_5)p + T_4 T_6 p^2].$$

From this result the value of $\psi_d$ is obtained:

$$\psi_d = \left[\frac{1 + (T_4 + T_5)p + T_4 T_6 p^2}{1 + (T_1 + T_2)p + T_1 T_3 p^2}\right] L_d i_d$$

$$+ \left[\frac{1 + T_{kd}p}{1 + (T_1 + T_2)p + T_1 T_3 p^2}\right] \frac{L_{md}e_f}{r_f}. \quad \ldots(6.20)$$

The values of the constants in this expression are given below. They are expressed in terms of the reactances, each denoted by the symbol $x$ with an appropriate suffix, and each equal to the corresponding inductance multiplied by $\omega$, as listed on page 122.

$$T_1 = \frac{1}{\omega r_f}(x_{md} + x_f),$$

$$T_2 = \frac{1}{\omega r_{kd}}(x_{md} + x_{kd}),$$

$$T_3 = \frac{1}{\omega r_{kd}}\left(x_{kd} + \frac{x_{md}x_f}{x_{md} + x_f}\right),$$

$$T_4 = \frac{1}{\omega r_f}\left(x_f + \frac{x_{md}x_a}{x_{md} + x_a}\right),$$

$$T_5 = \frac{1}{\omega r_{kd}}\left(x_{kd} + \frac{x_{md}x_a}{x_{md} + x_a}\right),$$

$$T_6 = \frac{1}{\omega r_{kd}}\left(x_{kd} + \frac{x_{md}x_f x_a}{x_{md}x_a + x_{md}x_f + x_a x_f}\right),$$

$$T_{kd} = \frac{x_{kd}}{\omega r_{kd}},$$

$$L_d = L_{md} + l_a.$$

The values of $x_d(p)$ and $G(p)$ for the synchronous machine with one damper coil on each axis are found by comparing Eqns. (6.11) and (6.20) and equating coefficients. Expressions for $x_d(p)$ and $G(p)$ can then be obtained in the form:

$$x_d(p) = \frac{(1 + T_d'p)(1 + T_d''p)}{(1 + T_{d0}'p)(1 + T_{d0}''p)} x_d, \qquad \ldots(6.21)$$

$$G(p) = \frac{(1 + T_{kd}p)}{(1 + T_{d0}'p)(1 + T_{d0}''p)} \frac{x_{md}}{r_f}, \qquad \ldots(6.22)$$

where the new constants are determined by the identities:

$$(1 + T_{d0}'p)(1 + T_{d0}''p) \equiv 1 + (T_1 + T_2)p + T_1 T_3 p^2, \qquad \ldots(6.23)$$

$$(1 + T_d'p)(1 + T_d''p) \equiv 1 + (T_4 + T_5)p + T_4 T_6 p^2. \qquad \ldots(6.24)$$

The four new constants $T_{d0}'$, $T_{d0}''$, $T_d'$, $T_d''$ are the four principal time constants of the synchronous machine. Their values can be calculated accurately by solving two quadratic equations. More usually the values are calculated by making a further approximation, based on the fact that the per-unit resistance of the damper winding is generally much larger than that of the field winding. $T_2$ and $T_3$ are then much less than $T_1$, and the right-hand side of Eqn. (6.23) differs very little from $(1+T_1p)(1+T_3p)$. Hence $T_{d0}'$ and $T_{d0}''$ are approximately equal to $T_1$ and $T_3$ respectively. Similarly $T_d'$ and $T_d''$ are approximately equal to $T_4$ and $T_6$. These approximate values are given in the list on page 122, together with the names of the four time constants.

The value of $x_q(p)$ is obtained by eliminating $i_{kq}$ from Eqns. (6.18) and comparing the result with Eqn. (6.14):

$$x_q(p) = \frac{1+T_q''p}{1+T_{q0}''p} x_q, \qquad \ldots(6.25)$$

where $T_{q0}''$ and $T_q''$ have the values given on page 122.

*Summary of the equations for the synchronous machine with one damper winding on each axis*

For the study of practical synchronous machine problems it is often more convenient to retain the quantities $\psi_d$ and $\psi_q$ instead of using Eqns. (6.19). This method is used for all the problems dealt with in Chaps. VII to X. With the approximations made in the present section the equations are as follows:

$$\left.\begin{aligned} e_d &= p\psi_d + v\psi_q + r_a i_d \\ e_q &= -v\psi_d + p\psi_q + r_a i_q \end{aligned}\right\}, \qquad \ldots(6.7)$$

$$f_e = \frac{\omega}{2}(\psi_d i_q - \psi_q i_d), \qquad \ldots(6.8)$$

$$\psi_d = \frac{x_d(p)}{\omega} i_d + \frac{G(p)}{\omega} e_f, \qquad \ldots(6.11)$$

$$\psi_q = \frac{x_q(p)}{\omega} i_q, \qquad \ldots(6.14)$$

where

$$x_d(p) = \frac{(1+T_d'p)(1+T_d''p)}{(1+T_{d0}'p)(1+T_{d0}''p)} x_d, \qquad \ldots(6.21)$$

$$G(p) = \frac{(1+T_{kd}p)}{(1+T_{d0}'p)(1+T_{d0}''p)} \frac{x_{md}}{r_f}, \qquad \ldots(6.22)$$

$$x_q(p) = \frac{(1+T_q''p)}{(1+T_{q0}''p)} x_q. \qquad \ldots(6.25)$$

121

*The constants of the synchronous machine*

The following table contains a list of the fundamental constants and gives formulae for the constants in the above equations. A few other quantities, which are introduced in later chapters, are also included. All are per-unit values; $\omega$ is the synchronous speed of the machine in electrical radians per second. Against each quantity is given the name by which it is known in the usually accepted terminology. Some of the terms have already been defined, while others are explained in later sections, particularly in connection with the problem of the sudden short circuit discussed in Chap. VIII.

Many of the terms used are defined in Ref. 41.1. Some methods of calculating the constants are given in Ref. 31.1, and the tests used for determining them experimentally are described in Refs. 31.2 and 45.4.

*Fundamental machine constants*

$r_a$ =armature resistance.

$r_f$ =field resistance.

$r_{kd}$ =direct-axis damper resistance.

$r_{kq}$ =quadrature-axis damper resistance.

$x_{md}=\omega L_{md}$=direct-axis magnetising reactance.

$x_{mq}=\omega L_{mq}$=quadrature-axis magnetising reactance.

$x_a =\omega l_a$ =armature leakage reactance.

$x_f =\omega l_f$ =field leakage reactance.

$x_{kd}=\omega l_{kd}$ =direct-axis damper leakage reactance.

$x_{kq}=\omega l_{kq}$ =quadrature-axis damper leakage reactance.

*Time constants*

$$T_{d0}' =\frac{1}{\omega r_f}(x_f+x_{md})$$

=direct-axis transient open-circuit time constant.

$$T_d' =\frac{1}{\omega r_f}\left(x_f+\frac{x_{md}x_a}{x_{md}+x_a}\right)$$

=direct-axis transient short-circuit time constant.

$$T_{d0}'' = \frac{1}{\omega r_{kd}}\left(x_{kd} + \frac{x_{md}x_f}{x_{md}+x_f}\right)$$

=direct-axis subtransient open-circuit time constant.

$$T_d'' = \frac{1}{\omega r_{kd}}\left(x_{kd} + \frac{x_{md}x_a x_f}{x_{md}x_a + x_{md}x_f + x_a x_f}\right)$$

=direct-axis subtransient short-circuit time constant.

$$T_{q0}'' = \frac{1}{\omega r_{kq}}(x_{kq}+x_{mq})$$

=quadrature-axis subtransient open-circuit time constant.

$$T_q'' = \frac{1}{\omega r_{kq}}\left(x_{kq} + \frac{x_{mq}x_a}{x_{mq}+x_a}\right)$$

=quadrature-axis subtransient short-circuit time constant.

$$T_{kd} = \frac{x_{kd}}{\omega r_{kd}}$$

=direct-axis damper leakage time constant.

*Derived reactances*

$$x_d = x_a + x_{md}$$

=direct-axis synchronous reactance.

$$x_d' = x_a\frac{T_d'}{T_{d0}'} = x_a + \frac{x_{md}x_f}{x_{md}+x_f}$$

=direct-axis transient reactance.

$$x_d'' = x_a\frac{T_d'T_d''}{T_{d0}'T_{d0}''} = x_a + \frac{x_{md}x_f x_{kd}}{x_{md}x_f + x_{md}x_{kd} + x_f x_{kd}}$$

=direct-axis subtransient reactance.

$$x_q = x_a + x_{mq}$$

=quadrature-axis synchronous reactance.

$$x_q'' = x_q\frac{T_q''}{T_{q0}''} = x_a + \frac{x_{mq}x_{kq}}{x_{mq}+x_{kq}}$$

=quadrature-axis subtransient reactance.

It may be noted that the notation, adopted above for the synchronous machine, while agreeing in general with that used

123

in earlier publications, differs from it in respect to a few symbols where the earlier notation was rather illogical. The armature leakage is here denoted by $x_a$ to correspond with the resistance $r_a$, and the magnetising reactances are $x_{md}$ and $x_{mq}$. Corresponding suffixes are used for the inductances. The small letter $x$ is used for all reactances, following the established notation, as already mentioned on page 95, but the leakage inductances are distinguished from the mutual or complete inductances by using the small letter $l$ for leakage inductances and the capital letter $L$ for the magnetising inductances (see page 19).

### 26. General Equations of the Induction Motor

The induction motor has a uniform air-gap and both of its windings are A.C. windings distributed in slots. The great majority of practical induction motors have the primary winding on the stator and the secondary winding on the rotor, but the reversed arrangement is sometimes used. Because of the uniform air-gap, two alternative theoretical treatments are possible, according to whether the primary or secondary winding is assumed to rotate, and either theory can apply to either practical arrangement.

If the primary winding of the idealised machine is on the rotating part, the induction motor can be considered as a special case of the synchronous machine, and the equations are those of Eqns. (6.19) in a simplified form. If, on the other hand, the primary winding is stationary, different equations are obtained and different transformations are needed. The equations in this form were first given by Kron (Ref. 35.1). The derivation of the equations is discussed in Ref. 38.1.

*Park's equations for the induction motor*

The diagram for an idealised induction motor with the primary winding rotating is shown in Fig. 43, in which the suffixes 1 and 2 are used to denote primary and secondary. Because of the uniform air-gap, corresponding inductances are the same on both axes. $e_{d2}$ and $e_{q2}$ are 'injected voltages' impressed on the secondary winding from outside. For the ordinary induction motor with a short-circuited secondary

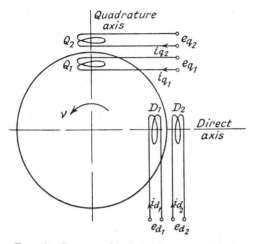

FIG. 43.—Diagram of an induction motor with the primary winding on the rotor.

winding, $e_{d2}$ and $e_{q2}$ are both zero. The voltage and torque equations are:

| $e_{d2}$ | $=$ | $r_{d2}+L_2 p$ | $Mp$ | | | $\cdot$ | $i_{d2}$ |
|---|---|---|---|---|---|---|---|
| $e_{d1}$ | | $Mp$ | $r_{d1}+L_1 p$ | $L_1\nu$ | $M\nu$ | | $i_{d1}$ |
| $e_{q1}$ | | $-M\nu$ | $-L_1\nu$ | $r_{q1}+L_1 p$ | $Mp$ | | $i_{q1}$ |
| $e_{q2}$ | | | | $Mp$ | $r_{q2}+L_2 p$ | | $i_{q2}$ |

$$\ldots(6.26)$$

$$f_e = \frac{\omega}{2}(Mi_{d2}i_{q1} - Mi_{d1}i_{q2}). \qquad \ldots(6.27)$$

For a three-phase rotor winding, the transformations between the fictitious axis quantities and the actual phase values in this winding are those given in Eqns. (6.1) to (6.4), with an additional suffix 1 on each voltage and current. On the secondary side, the axis voltages and currents in the equations would be the actual values if the winding were a two-phase winding with phase $D2$ located on the direct axis. Generally, however, the

125

secondary winding is either a three-phase winding or a squirrel cage, and a transformation is needed to relate the voltages and currents to those in an equivalent two-phase winding. For a stationary three-phase winding in which phase $A$ is located on the direct axis, the transformations are given by Eqns. (6.28) to (6.31), except that an additional suffix 2 is required on each voltage and current. These equations are obtained from Eqns. (6.1) to (6.4) by putting $\theta=0$.

$$
\begin{bmatrix} e_d \\ e_q \\ e_0 \end{bmatrix} = \frac{2}{3} \begin{bmatrix} 1 & -\frac{1}{2} & -\frac{1}{2} \\ 0 & -\frac{\sqrt{3}}{2} & \frac{\sqrt{3}}{2} \\ \frac{1}{2} & \frac{1}{2} & \frac{1}{2} \end{bmatrix} \cdot \begin{bmatrix} e_a \\ e_b \\ e_c \end{bmatrix} \qquad \ldots(6.28)
$$

$$
\begin{bmatrix} e_a \\ e_b \\ e_c \end{bmatrix} = \begin{bmatrix} 1 & 0 & 1 \\ -\frac{1}{2} & -\frac{\sqrt{3}}{2} & 1 \\ -\frac{1}{2} & \frac{\sqrt{3}}{2} & 1 \end{bmatrix} \cdot \begin{bmatrix} e_d \\ e_q \\ e_0 \end{bmatrix} \qquad \ldots(6.29)
$$

$$
\begin{bmatrix} i_d \\ i_q \\ i_0 \end{bmatrix} = \frac{2}{3} \begin{bmatrix} 1 & -\frac{1}{2} & -\frac{1}{2} \\ 0 & -\frac{\sqrt{3}}{2} & \frac{\sqrt{3}}{2} \\ \frac{1}{2} & \frac{1}{2} & \frac{1}{2} \end{bmatrix} \cdot \begin{bmatrix} i_a \\ i_b \\ i_c \end{bmatrix} \qquad \ldots(6.30)
$$

$$\begin{vmatrix} i_a \\ i_b \\ i_c \end{vmatrix} = \begin{vmatrix} 1 & 0 & 1 \\ -\dfrac{1}{2} & -\dfrac{\sqrt{3}}{2} & 1 \\ -\dfrac{1}{2} & \dfrac{\sqrt{3}}{2} & 1 \end{vmatrix} \cdot \begin{vmatrix} i_d \\ i_q \\ i_0 \end{vmatrix} \qquad \dots(6.31)$$

*Kron's equations for the induction motor*

The alternative arrangement, in which the primary winding is stationary, is shown in Fig. 44. It corresponds to the normal arrangement of a practical motor, and is usually the more

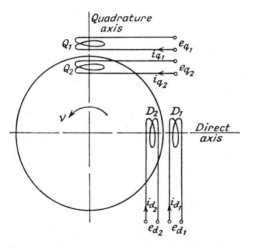

Fig. 44.—Diagram of an induction motor with the primary winding on the stator.

convenient one for analytical purposes, particularly when the secondary winding is short-circuited. The only essential difference compared with Fig. 43 is that the primary and secondary applied voltages are changed over. The form of the generalised equations is therefore exactly as before with the suffixes interchanged. The voltage and torque equations are:

| $e_{d1}$ | = | $r_{d1}+L_1 p$ | $Mp$ | | | $\cdot$ | $i_{d1}$ |
|---|---|---|---|---|---|---|---|
| $e_{d2}$ | | $Mp$ | $r_{d2}+L_2 p$ | $L_2 \nu$ | $M\nu$ | | $i_{d2}$ |
| $e_{q2}$ | | $-M\nu$ | $-L_2 \nu$ | $r_{q2}+L_2 p$ | $Mp$ | | $i_{q2}$ |
| $e_{q1}$ | | | | $Mp$ | $r_{q1}+L_1 p$ | | $i_{q1}$ |

$$\ldots(6.32)$$

$$f_e = \frac{\omega}{2}\left(M i_{d1} i_{q2} - M i_{d2} i_{q1}\right). \qquad \ldots(6.33)$$

The primary transformations are now Eqns. (6.28) to (6.31) with suffix 1, and the secondary transformations are Eqns. (6.1) to (6.4) with suffix 2.

### Squirrel-cage windings

Any possible arrangement of squirrel-cage bars and end-rings, including double squirrel cages, can be dealt with by a method similar to that explained on page 112. However, any squirrel-cage winding with $m$ equally spaced bars forming an $m$-phase winding can be treated much more simply by transforming it into an equivalent two-phase winding. For a rotating winding, the direct and quadrature axis voltages are:

$$\left.\begin{aligned}
e_d &= \frac{2}{m}\left[e_a \cos\theta + e_b \cos\left(\theta - \frac{2\pi}{m}\right) + \ldots + e_m \cos\left(\theta - \frac{2(m-1)\pi}{m}\right)\right] \\
e_q &= \frac{2}{m}\left[e_a \sin\theta + e_b \sin\left(\theta - \frac{2\pi}{m}\right) + \ldots + e_m \sin\left(\theta - \frac{2(m-1)\pi}{m}\right)\right]
\end{aligned}\right\}$$

$$\ldots(6.34)$$

For a stationary winding, the values can be obtained from Eqns. (6.34) by putting $\theta = 0$.

In order to define the set of variables completely it would be necessary to specify additional voltages and currents, $(m-2)$ in number, corresponding to the zero-sequence quantities $e_0$ and

$i_0$ in the three-phase case. These components are similar to the quantities obtained when resolving an $m$-phase system into symmetrical components, and are determined by independent equations. The actual squirrel-cage winding consists of many coupled circuits interconnected through the end-rings, each circuit being strictly a mesh in a network and each current being the current in a bar. Since the impressed voltage in every circuit is zero, all the symmetrical component voltages are also zero. Consequently all the current components except $i_d$ and $i_q$ are also zero. Hence the squirrel cage is equivalent to the two-phase winding formed by coils $D2$ and $Q2$ in Fig. 44, and for most purposes it is not necessary to introduce the actual currents at all.

The equations of a double squirrel-cage induction motor can be written down by including an additional pair of two-phase coils in Fig. 43 or 44 and adding two more voltage equations.

### 27. Application of the Equations to A.C. Machine Problems

It has already been pointed out that, although the general equations derived in this chapter apply for all possible conditions of operation, it is not feasible to obtain a completely general solution. In Chaps. VII to X several definite problems of limited range are discussed in detail, following the lines of the classification of Table 1, page 36. For each problem the particular conditions relating to the applied voltages, the speed, or the boundary conditions of a transient problem, must first be set out and substituted into the general equations, from which the particular solution can then be found. The problems discussed in the following chapters are typical of the practical problems that can be handled in this way, but no claim is made that the treatment is comprehensive. The aim is rather to explain the method so that a reader can more readily explore other examples to be found in earlier publications, or pursue the study of some of the many hitherto unsolved problems.

In order to obtain a solution of practical value it is necessary to make approximations wherever possible, and the more complicated the condition the more far-reaching must be the approximations. For some of the simpler problems discussed a fairly complete solution can be obtained, making only a few approximations based, for example, on the knowledge that the resistances or other quantities are small. Chaps. VII to IX are concerned with these problems, which relate mainly to a single machine operating in conjunction with a fixed supply system. For more complicated problems, relating to larger systems, in which several generators are interconnected with other apparatus, the much more drastic approximations used in Chap. X become necessary.

When the supply voltage is specified as one of the governing conditions of the problem, the known applied voltages are the actual phase values, and the first step in the analysis is to determine the axis voltages for insertion in the equations. In an important class of problems the speed can be assumed to be constant and the equations for the axis currents become linear differential equations with constant coefficients. The problems discussed in Chaps. VII and VIII are of this type.

If, in the equations, all the applied voltages are either D.C. or A.C. of a common frequency, the equations can be converted into real or complex algebraic equations by making the appropriate substitution for the operator $p$. For this purpose, however the decisive question is the frequency of the axis voltages and currents, not the frequency of the actual phase quantities. Steady synchronous operation of the synchronous machine, for which the axis voltages have steady D.C. values, is considered in Sect. 28, while non-synchronous operation, for which the axis voltages are of slip frequency, is dealt with in Sects. 30 and 31.

For a transient condition, for which it can be assumed that the speed remains constant after a definite sudden change of axis voltage, the Heaviside operational method can be used to determine the transient currents. The assumption of constant speed is a reasonable one if the changes are rapid. The calculation of the transient currents and torque in a machine connected to a balanced external circuit is discussed at some length in Chap. VIII.

The analysis of the problems considered in Chaps. VII and VIII is based on the assumption that the speed remains constant. Chap. IX is devoted to some problems for which this assumption does not hold. The more general type of problem, considered in Sect. 36, can only be handled accurately by means of a computational method applied to a particular numerical case, using, for example, a differential analyser. The oscillation problems of Sects. 37 and 38, in which the speed and all the other quantities oscillate about a condition of steady operation, are analysed as A.C. problems by means of complex number equations.

The methods discussed in Chaps. VII to IX lead to reasonably accurate solutions, but the working is often laborious even for relatively simple problems. Moreover the range of problems that can be dealt with in this way is limited. In Chap. X some simplified methods, using different degrees of approximation, are explained. Sect. 40 deals with problems in which the three-phase circuits are balanced, and explains the basis of the simplified machine theory used in modern methods of power-system analysis. The analysis of unbalanced conditions is considered in Sect. 41, which gives a brief résumé both of the exact mathematical theory and of the approximate methods used for this condition. Finally, Sect. 42 contains a summary of the practical methods used in analysing the various problems arising in the operation of power systems.

# CHAPTER VII

# A.C. Operation of Synchronous and Induction Machines

## 28. Steady Operation of the Synchronous Machine at Synchronous Speed

In Sect. 21 the vector diagram and vector equation of a three-phase synchronous machine were derived by considering the rotating M.M.F. wave set up by the armature currents. In the present section the same result is deduced as a special case from the general equations.

During normal steady A.C. operation, the speed of the machine is the constant synchronous speed $\omega$. The field voltage and current are constant, the damper currents are zero, and the armature phase voltages and currents are balanced three-phase quantities. Hence, if zero time is taken as the instant when phase $A$ is on the direct axis:

$$\nu = \omega,$$
$$\theta = \omega t,$$
$$e_0 = i_0 = 0.$$

From the transformation equations (6.2) and (6.4), the voltage and current in phase $A$ are:

$$e_a = e_d \cos \omega t + e_q \sin \omega t,$$
$$i_a = i_d \cos \omega t + i_q \sin \omega t.$$

Now if the voltage and current in phase $A$ are represented by vectors $\mathbf{E}$ and $\mathbf{I}$, as in Fig. 36, the components of the vectors are related to the axis quantities as shown below. The component vectors of current are indicated in Fig. 36 by the symbols $\mathbf{I}_d$ and $\mathbf{I}_q$ in heavy type. Let the magnitudes of the components be denoted by $I_d$ and $I_q$ in ordinary type. Then

$$\mathbf{I} = \mathbf{I}_d + \mathbf{I}_q = I_d + jI_q.$$

132

Hence

$$\mathbf{I}_d = I_d + j \cdot 0,$$
$$\mathbf{I}_q = 0 + jI_q.$$

Similarly let the magnitudes of the components of voltage be $\mathbf{E}_d$ and $\mathbf{E}_q$.

$$i_a = Re\{\sqrt{2}(I_d + jI_q)\varepsilon^{j\omega t}\}$$
$$= \sqrt{2}(I_d \cos \omega t - I_q \sin \omega t),$$
$$e_a = \sqrt{2}(E_d \cos \omega t - E_q \sin \omega t).$$

Since both pairs of relations hold for all values of $t$, it follows, by equating coefficients, that

$$i_d = \sqrt{2}I_d, \qquad i_q = -\sqrt{2}I_q,$$
$$e_d = \sqrt{2}E_d, \qquad e_q = -\sqrt{2}E_q.$$

Hence for steady operation at synchronous speed the axis voltages and currents are all constant quantities independent of time. Moreover $e_f$ and $i_f$ are constant and $e_{kd}$, $e_{kq}$, $i_{kd}$, $i_{kq}$ are all zero. The general equations (6.19) can therefore be simplified, putting $p=0$, and $\nu = \omega$, and using the synchronous reactances $x_d$, $x_q$, defined on page 123:

$$\left. \begin{array}{l} e_f = r_f i_f \\ e_d = r_a i_d + x_q i_q \\ e_q = -x_{md} i_f - x_d i_d + r_a i_q \end{array} \right\} . \qquad \ldots(7.1)$$

Hence

$$\mathbf{E} = E_d + jE_q$$
$$= \frac{1}{\sqrt{2}}(e_d - je_q)$$
$$= \frac{1}{\sqrt{2}}[r_a(i_d - ji_q) + x_q i_q + jx_d i_d + jx_{md} i_f]$$
$$= r_a(I_d + jI_q) + jx_d I_d - x_q I_q + \frac{jx_{md} i_f}{\sqrt{2}}$$
$$= r_a \mathbf{I} + jx_d \mathbf{I}_d + jx_q \mathbf{I}_q + \mathbf{E}_0, \qquad \ldots(7.2)$$

where $\mathbf{E}_0 = \dfrac{jx_{md} i_f}{\sqrt{2}}$, the no-load voltage. Eqn. (7.2) is the same as Eqn. (5.5) on page 96.

The above analysis shows that for steady operation there is a direct relation between the axis values of voltage and current and the components of the vectors representing the phase values, and thus $I_d$ and $I_q$ are measurable quantities. The vector diagram is in fact generally derived, as in Sect. 21, by using the vector components. That method only applies, however, for A.C. conditions and cannot be used for general transient problems. When the phase voltages and currents do not vary sinusoidally with time the only way to replace them by axis quantities is to use the transformation equations (6.1) to (6.4).

## 29. Starting Conditions of A.C. Motors

In Sect. 30 the general equations are applied to an A.C. machine supplied with balanced three-phase voltages and running at a constant speed away from synchronism. This condition includes the normal steady operation of an induction motor and is also of considerable importance in analysing the behaviour of both induction motors and synchronous motors during starting. The analysis is based on Park's equations and applies directly to a synchronous machine with a damper winding on each axis in addition to the field winding. The results can be applied to an induction motor by treating it as a special case in which all the constants are the same for both axes.

In order to apply the analysis to the starting operation, it is necessary to make certain assumptions. The starting of a motor is initiated by switching on the supply when the motor is at rest. The starting operation is usually analysed by obtaining a torque-speed curve, which gives for each speed the torque that would be exerted if the motor ran steadily at that speed. Starting up is, however, a transient condition, during which the speed and all the other quantities are continually changing, and the instantaneous torque corresponding to any instantaneous speed actually differs to some extent from that determined in this way. If the rate of rise of speed is not too rapid the error is not great (see Ref. 44.3).

In an induction motor the speed rises smoothly until it settles down to the steady value just below synchronism. It is usually assumed that the torque exerted as the motor runs up is the same as that given by the torque-speed curve based on steady conditions. The method is accepted as a reliable way of studying the behaviour of an induction motor when starting up.

A synchronous motor, when switched on to the A.C. supply, runs up in a similar manner, with the damper and field windings acting like the secondary circuits of an induction motor. It cannot, however (apart from the effect of the small 'reluctance torque' in a salient-pole machine), attain synchronous speed until a direct-current excitation in the field winding causes it to pull into step. The starting conditions are thus a good deal more complicated for the synchronous motor than for the induction motor. There are two possibilities:

1. If the field winding is connected to an exciter, which provides a voltage right from the time when the motor is at rest, the motor synchronises without any further control operation.

2. If there is no exciter voltage in the field circuit during the running-up period, this excitation voltage must be brought up to a sufficient value before the motor can synchronise. The field winding is usually closed through a resistance during starting, in order to limit the induced voltage when the motor is at a standstill. The synchronising operation either switches in the exciter or, if the exciter armature has been included in the alternator field circuit, it switches on the exciter field.

The starting of a synchronous motor must therefore be considered in two parts—running-up and synchronising. The running-up period can be dealt with, in the same way as for the induction motor, by obtaining a torque-speed curve giving the torque that would be exerted if the motor ran at a constant speed. The method of calculating the torque-speed curve is given in Sect. 30. The synchronising problem, which can only be dealt with as a true transient problem, is discussed in Sect. 36.

An induction motor running at a steady speed away from synchronism exerts a constant torque, but a synchronous motor, because of the lack of symmetry in the field circuits, develops a pulsating torque. Only the mean torque is of use in starting the motor, and consequently, in deriving the torque-speed curve, only the mean torque is considered.

The calculation of Sect. 30 assumes that the applied voltage

135

in the field circuit is zero. If there were an exciter voltage $e_f$ in the field circuit there would be additional currents in the machine, which, by the principle of superposition, could be determined separately by assuming the armature voltage to be zero. The superimposed currents are those of a short-circuited alternator operating at the appropriate frequency and produce a braking torque. For this reason synchronous motors are usually started up with the field unexcited.

### 30. The Torque-speed Curve of the Synchronous Motor

If the machine runs with a constant slip $s$, and the value of $\theta$ at zero time is $\lambda$, then:

$$\nu = (1-s)\omega,$$
$$\theta = (1-s)\omega t + \lambda.$$

With balanced A.C. voltages the zero-sequence voltage $e_0$ is zero. From the transformation equation (6.2) the voltage in phase $A$ is related to the axis voltages by:

$$e_a = e_d \cos \{(1-s)\omega t + \lambda\} + e_q \sin \{(1-s)\omega t + \lambda\}.$$

The applied voltage is specified to be a sinusoidal voltage at frequency $\omega/2\pi$. Hence if the phase is given by an angle $\lambda'$, the voltage of phase $A$ can be expressed as:

$$e_a = E_m \cos (\omega t + \lambda').$$

For an A.C. problem the instant of zero time can be chosen arbitrarily. In the present instance, the working is considerably simplified if zero time is chosen so that $\lambda = \lambda'$. The second expression for $e_a$ can then be written:

$$e_a = E_m[\cos s\omega t \cos \{(1-s)\omega t + \lambda\} - \sin s\omega t \sin \{(1-s)\omega t + \lambda\}].$$

The two values of $e_a$ must be identical for all values of $t$. Hence by equating coefficients:

$$e_d = E_m \cos s\omega t,$$
$$e_q = -E_m \sin s\omega t.$$

It is also specified that the field voltage is zero; $e_f = 0$.

Thus when the synchronous motor runs with the slip $s$, and has an applied three-phase voltage of supply frequency, the phase currents alternate at supply frequency, but the axis currents alternate at slip frequency. The currents in the field and damper windings, which act like the secondary of an induction motor, also alternate at slip frequency.

## General equations

With the above values substituted in them, the general equations (6.7), (6.11) and (6.14) become:

$$E_m \cos s\omega t = p\psi_d + (1-s)\omega\psi_q + r_a i_d \left.\right\} \qquad ...(7.3)$$
$$-E_m \sin s\omega t = -(1-s)\omega\psi_d + p\psi_q + r_a i_q$$

where $\psi_d = \dfrac{x_d(p)}{\omega} i_d$

$\psi_q = \dfrac{x_q(p)}{\omega} i_q.$

## Vector equations for A.C. operation

Eqns. (7.3) are linear differential equations with sinusoidal applied voltages of slip frequency $s\omega/2\pi$. Hence there is a steady A.C. solution for which the axis quantities $i_d$, $i_q$, $\psi_d$, $\psi_q$ all alternate at slip frequency. The complex numbers representing the axis voltages can be deduced by putting $e_d$ and $e_q$ in the form:

$$e_d = Re\{E_m \varepsilon^{js\omega t}\} = Re\{\sqrt{2}\mathbf{E}_d \varepsilon^{js\omega t}\},$$
$$e_q = Re\{jE_m \varepsilon^{js\omega t}\} = Re\{\sqrt{2}\mathbf{E}_q \varepsilon^{js\omega t}\},$$

and hence:

$$\mathbf{E}_d = \frac{E_m}{\sqrt{2}} + j.0 = E \text{ (say)},$$

$$\mathbf{E}_q = 0 + j\frac{E_m}{\sqrt{2}} = jE,$$

where $E$ is a scalar quantity whose magnitude is the R.M.S. value of the supply voltage.

The vector equations are obtained by substituting $p = js\omega$ in Eqns. (7.3) and replacing the small letters by capitals in heavy type:

$$E = js\omega\mathbf{\Psi}_d + (1-s)\omega\mathbf{\Psi}_q + r_a\mathbf{I}_d \left.\right\} \qquad ...(7.4)$$
$$jE = -(1-s)\omega\mathbf{\Psi}_d + js\omega\mathbf{\Psi}_q + r_a\mathbf{I}_q$$

where
$$\left.\begin{array}{l} \omega\mathbf{\Psi}_d = x_d(js\omega)\mathbf{I}_d \\ \omega\mathbf{\Psi}_q = x_q(js\omega)\mathbf{I}_q \end{array}\right\}. \qquad \ldots(7.5)$$

The mean torque $F_e$ can be deduced from Eqn. (6.8) if the expression is modified so as to apply to the A.C. condition, as explained on page 43:

$$F_e = \frac{\omega}{2} Re\{\mathbf{\Psi}_d{}^*\mathbf{I}_q - \mathbf{\Psi}_q{}^*\mathbf{I}_d\}. \qquad \ldots(7.6)$$

The mean motoring torque $F_m$ is equal and opposite to $F_e$ and is given by:

$$F_m = \frac{\omega}{2} Re\{\mathbf{\Psi}_q{}^*\mathbf{I}_d - \mathbf{\Psi}_d{}^*\mathbf{I}_q\}, \qquad \ldots(7.7)$$

where $\mathbf{\Psi}_d{}^*$ and $\mathbf{\Psi}_q{}^*$ are the complex conjugates of $\mathbf{\Psi}_d$ and $\mathbf{\Psi}_q$.

*Torque-speed curve with primary resistance neglected*

If $r_a$ is neglected the voltage equations in (7.4) reduce to:

$$E = js\omega\mathbf{\Psi}_d + (1-s)\omega\mathbf{\Psi}_q,$$
$$jE = -(1-s)\omega\mathbf{\Psi}_d + js\omega\mathbf{\Psi}_q,$$

whence $\omega\mathbf{\Psi}_d = -jE$,
$\omega\mathbf{\Psi}_q = E$.

Substituting in Eqn. (7.7), the mean motoring torque is:

$$F_m = \frac{E^2}{2} Re\left\{\frac{1}{jx_d(js\omega)} + \frac{1}{jx_q(js\omega)}\right\}, \qquad \ldots(7.8)$$

$$= F_{md} + F_{mq}, \qquad \ldots(7.9)$$

where

$$\left.\begin{array}{l} F_{md} = \dfrac{E^2}{2} Re\left\{\dfrac{1}{\mathbf{Z}_d}\right\} \\[2mm] F_{mq} = \dfrac{E^2}{2} Re\left\{\dfrac{1}{\mathbf{Z}_q}\right\} \end{array}\right\}, \qquad \ldots(7.10)$$

$$\left.\begin{array}{l} \mathbf{Z}_d = jx_d(js\omega) = j\,\dfrac{(1+js\omega T_d{}')(1+js\omega T_d{}'')}{(1+js\omega T_{d0}{}')(1+js\omega T_{d0}{}'')}\,x_d \\[3mm] \mathbf{Z}_q = jx_q(js\omega) = j\,\dfrac{(1+js\omega T_q{}'')}{(1+js\omega T_{q0}{}'')}\,x_q \end{array}\right\}, \ldots(7.11)$$

using the expanded expressions for $x_d(p)$ and $x_q(p)$ in Eqns. (6.21) and (6.26).

The torque is thus the sum of two quantities, each of which is a torque associated with one axis only. A typical torque-speed curve of a synchronous motor, calculated by the above method, is shown on Fig. 45, where the thick line gives the total mean torque $F_m$ and the thin lines give the two component torques $F_{md}$ and $F_{mq}$.

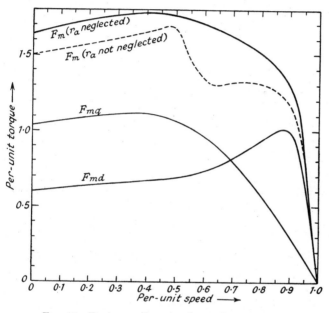

Fig. 45.—Torque-speed curves of a synchronous motor.

*Equivalent circuits*

The operational equivalent circuits of Fig. 42 can be converted into A.C. equivalent circuits by substituting $p = js\omega$ and replacing small by capital symbols for the variables, as in the equations. If in addition the two applied voltages and all the impedances are divided by $s$, and $e_f$ is put equal to zero, the equivalent circuits of Fig. 46 are obtained. It is evident that the overall impedance of the direct-axis circuit (Fig. 46($a$)) is $\mathbf{Z}_d$, since, from Eqns. (7.5):

$$j\omega\mathbf{\Psi}_d = jx_d(js\omega)\mathbf{I}_d = \mathbf{Z}_d\mathbf{I}_d.$$

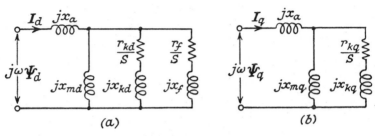

FIG. 46.—Equivalent circuits for calculating the torque-speed curve
of a synchronous motor.
(*a*) Direct axis.                    (*b*) Quadrature axis.

Similarly the impedance of the quadrature-axis circuit (Fig. 46($b$)) is $\mathbf{Z}_q$.

In order to calculate the torque-speed curve of a synchronous motor, it is simpler to use the equivalent circuits instead of the formulae in Eqn. (7.8). The method is then similar to that commonly used for the induction motor, except that two calculations must be made. The quadrature-axis circuit (Fig. 46($b$)) is similar to the equivalent circuit of the induction motor (Fig. 31) with the primary resistance neglected. Fig. 46($a$) is similar to the equivalent circuit of a double squirrel-cage induction motor with two secondary circuits. Thus each of the component torques is calculated from the appropriate equivalent circuit in the same way as for an induction motor.

If the above results are applied to an induction motor, treated as a special case in which there is no field winding and all the constants for the direct and quadrature axes are the same, the two equivalent circuits become identical. Hence only one circuit is needed, and the torque calculated from it is the required induction motor torque.

By using the equivalent circuit method, it is easy to obtain a more accurate determination of the torque of those synchronous machines for which the simplifications introduced in Sect. 25 would cause too much error. It is not difficult to set up more elaborate equivalent circuits to allow for the distribution of the squirrel-cage bars, or the effect of a field collar or a solid rotor spider. Such features may in some cases have an important effect on the motor characteristics. The more complicated equivalent circuits require more lengthy computations, for which the use of a network analyser may be necessary. The problem is discussed fully in Ref. 30.1.

The curve for $F_{mq}$ in Fig. 45(b) is that of an induction motor with a high per-unit secondary resistance determined by that of the damper winding, while the curve for $F_{md}$ is that of a motor with a low per-unit secondary resistance determined mainly by that of the field winding. $F_{mq}$ contributes most to the standstill starting torque, while $F_{md}$ has most influence in determining the slip when the motor is up to speed. The fact that $F_{md}$ and $F_{mq}$ differ indicates that there is a large pulsating torque which is important in determining whether the motor can pull into synchronism when the field is applied.

*Torque-speed curve allowing for primary resistance*

The torque-speed curve calculated by neglecting $r_a$ is accurate enough for many practical purposes. The curves obtained from tests of synchronous motors differ from the curves calculated by this method in having a double kink at about a half of synchronous speed, as shown dotted in Fig. 45. If the resistance is not neglected, the theoretical curve obtained by a more exact calculation shows a kink of this type. There is also an overall loss of torque when the resistance is taken into account.

Eqns. (7.4) can be rewritten, using Eqns. (7.5):

$$\left. \begin{aligned} E &= j(s + r_a\mathbf{Y}_d)\omega\mathbf{\Psi}_d + (1-s)\omega\mathbf{\Psi}_q \\ jE &= -(1-s)\omega\mathbf{\Psi}_d + j(s + r_a\mathbf{Y}_q)\omega\mathbf{\Psi}_q \end{aligned} \right\}, \qquad \ldots(7.12)$$

where

$$\left. \begin{aligned} \mathbf{Y}_d &= \frac{1}{jx_d(js\omega)} = \frac{1}{\mathbf{Z}_d} \\ \mathbf{Y}_q &= \frac{1}{jx_q(js\omega)} = \frac{1}{\mathbf{Z}_q} \end{aligned} \right\}. \qquad \ldots(7.13)$$

From Eqns. (7.7) and (7.12), the following expression is obtained for the mean torque:

$$F_m = \frac{E^2}{2|D|^2} \cdot Re\{(\mathbf{Y}_d + \mathbf{Y}_q) + \frac{r_a}{a}(2\mathbf{Y}_d\mathbf{Y}_q + |\mathbf{Y}_d|^2 + |\mathbf{Y}_q|^2)$$
$$+ \frac{r_a^2}{a^2}(\mathbf{Y}_q|\mathbf{Y}_d|^2 + \mathbf{Y}_d|\mathbf{Y}_q|^2)\} \Bigg\}, \quad ...(7.14)$$

where $D = 1 - s\dfrac{r_a}{a}(\mathbf{Y}_d + \mathbf{Y}_q) - \dfrac{r_a^2}{a}\mathbf{Y}_d\mathbf{Y}_q$,

$a = 1 - 2s$.

The dotted curve of Fig. 45 was calculated from Eqn. (7.14). The presence of the factor $a = (1 - 2s)$ in the denominator of some of the terms explains why the effect of $r_a$ is greater near to half speed, when the value of $a$ is small (see Ref. 51.2).

### 31. The Negative-sequence Reactances of a Synchronous Machine

In the application of symmetrical component theory to power-system analysis, a synchronous generator is assumed to have a definite negative-sequence reactance. The validity of this assumption and the determination of the appropriate value can be studied by the method of Sect. 30.

*Current due to negative-sequence voltage*

In a machine running at synchronous speed with negative-sequence applied voltages, the current is the same as it would be if the machine ran at a negative speed equal to synchronous speed and had positive-sequence applied voltages. Hence the theory of the last section applies with $s = 2$. With such a large slip the factors of the form $(1 + 2j\omega T)$ in the expressions $\mathbf{Z}_d$ and $\mathbf{Z}_q$ (Eqns. 7.11) can all be replaced approximately by $2j\omega T$, since $2\omega T$ is much greater than 1. Hence, if $r_a$ is neglected, Eqns. (7.5) give:

$$\mathbf{I}_d = \frac{-jE}{x_d(2j\omega)} = \frac{-jE}{x_d}\frac{T_{d0}'T_{d0}''}{T_d'T_d''} = -\frac{jE}{x_d''} \text{ (approx.)},$$

$$\mathbf{I}_q = \frac{E}{x_q(2j\omega)} = \frac{\mathbf{E}}{x_q}\frac{T_{q0}''}{T_q''} = \frac{E}{x_q''}.$$

In order to find the phase current $i_a$ the instantaneous axis currents $i_d$ and $i_q$ are determined as follows, putting $E = \dfrac{E_m}{\sqrt{2}}$:

$$i_d = Re\{\sqrt{2}\mathbf{I}_d \varepsilon^{2j\omega t}\} = \frac{E_m}{x_d''} \sin 2\omega t,$$

$$i_q = Re\{\sqrt{2}\mathbf{I}_q \varepsilon^{2j\omega t}\} = \frac{E_m}{x_q''} \cos 2\omega t.$$

Using the transformation equation (6.4) with $\theta = (-\omega t + \lambda)$:

$$\left. \begin{aligned} i_a &= E_m \left[ \frac{1}{x_d''} \sin 2\omega t \cos(\omega t - \lambda) - \frac{1}{x_q''} \cos 2\omega t \sin(\omega t - \lambda) \right] \\ &= \frac{E_m}{2} \left( \frac{1}{x_d''} + \frac{1}{x_q''} \right) \sin(\omega t + \lambda) + \frac{E_m}{2} \left( \frac{1}{x_d''} - \frac{1}{x_q''} \right) \sin(3\omega t - \lambda) \end{aligned} \right\}.$$

$$\dots(7.15)$$

The applied voltage is:

$$e_a = E_m \cos(\omega t + \lambda).$$

Thus the current due to the negative-sequence applied voltage contains a third harmonic in addition to the fundamental. If the fundamental only is considered, the effective negative-sequence reactance is:

$$x_{2e} = \frac{2x_d'' x_q''}{x_d'' + x_q''}. \qquad \dots(7.16)$$

*Voltage due to negative-sequence current*

The voltage due to balanced negative-sequence currents can be found by considering a machine running with slip $s = 2$, and carrying positive-sequence currents. If the same assumptions are now made for the current that were previously made for the voltage:

$$i_a = \mathbf{I}_m \cos(\omega t + \lambda),$$

$$\mathbf{I}_d = \frac{I_m}{\sqrt{2}} + j.0,$$

$$\mathbf{I}_q = 0 + j\frac{I_m}{\sqrt{2}}.$$

143

From Eqns. (7.4) with $s=2$, and $r_a$ neglected:

$$\mathbf{E}_d = 2j\omega\mathbf{\Psi}_d - \omega\mathbf{\Psi}_q,$$
$$\mathbf{E}_q = \omega\mathbf{\Psi}_d + 2j\omega\mathbf{\Psi}_q,$$

where, as before, $\omega\mathbf{\Psi}_d = x_d''\mathbf{I}_d,$
$\qquad\qquad\quad \omega\mathbf{\Psi}_q = x_q''\mathbf{I}_q.$

Hence

$$\mathbf{E}_d = j(2x_d'' - x_q'')\frac{I_m}{\sqrt{2}},$$

$$\mathbf{E}_q = (x_d'' - 2x_q'')\frac{I_m}{\sqrt{2}},$$

$$e_d = -I_m(2x_d'' - x_q'')\sin 2\omega t,$$
$$e_q = -I_m(2x_q'' - x_d'')\cos 2\omega t,$$

whence

$$e_a = -I_m[(2x_d'' - x_q'')\sin 2\omega t \cos(\omega t - \lambda)$$
$$- (2x_q'' - x_d'')\cos 2\omega t \sin(\omega t + \lambda)]$$
$$= -\frac{I_m}{2}(x_d'' + x_q'')\sin(\omega t + \lambda) - \frac{3I_m}{2}(x_d'' - x_q'')\cos(3\omega t + \lambda).$$
$$\dots(7.17)$$

Hence with balanced negative-sequence currents the voltage contains a third harmonic. The value of negative-sequence reactance based on the fundamental voltage is:

$$x_{2i} = \tfrac{1}{2}(x_d'' + x_q''). \qquad\qquad \dots(7.18)$$

*Value of negative-sequence reactance*

For the more general case of unbalanced conditions, when the external load is unbalanced, the appropriate value of negative-sequence reactance, defined as the ratio of fundamental voltage to fundamental current, is not necessarily either of the values determined above. The matter is discussed further in Sect. 41.

# CHAPTER VIII

# Symmetrical Short Circuit of an Alternator

## 32. Short Circuit of an Unloaded Alternator

Although the majority of the faults occurring in practice on a power system are unsymmetrical between the phases, the symmetrical fault is important because, although rarer, it is more severe. It is, moreover, a simpler condition to analyse, and therefore forms a suitable starting-point for a study of fault conditions. The short-circuit test, in which the three terminals of an unloaded alternator are all short-circuited simultaneously, is a well-established method of checking its transient charac-teristics. The present section gives a full analysis of a sudden symmetrical short circuit of an unloaded alternator, and the solution is then extended in Sect. 34 so that it can be applied to a loaded machine (see Ref. 51.7).

*The operational equations*

Let $t=0$ at the instant of short circuit, and let $\lambda$ be the angle between the axis of phase $A$ and the direct axis at that instant. The angle $\lambda$ defines the point in the A.C. cycle at which the short circuit occurs. Then, assuming that the speed has the constant value $\omega$:

$$\theta = \omega t + \lambda.$$

The notation used for the original steady quantities and for the superimposed values is that explained on page 68. The equations of page 133 hold for the steady values except that $\omega t$ is now replaced by $(\omega t + \lambda)$.

$$e_{a0} = \sqrt{2}[E_{d0} \cos (\omega t + \lambda) - E_{q0} \sin (\omega t + \lambda)]. \qquad ...(8.1)$$

Comparing this with the transformation equation

$$e_{a0} = e_{d0} \cos (\omega t + \lambda) + e_{q0} \sin (\omega t + \lambda),$$

it follows that

$$e_{d0} = \sqrt{2}E_{d0} = V_d,$$
$$e_{q0} = -\sqrt{2}E_{q0} = V_q.$$

145

The new symbols $V_d$ and $V_q$ are introduced to distinguish the voltages in the original steady state. $V_d$ and $V_q$ are the constant axis voltages and are equal in magnitude to the maximum values of the two components of the phase voltage given by Eqn. (8.1). The instantaneous values of the two components of $e_{a0}$ are therefore:

$$\left.\begin{array}{l} [e_{a0}]_d = V_d \cos{(\omega t + \lambda)} \\ [e_{a0}]_q = V_q \sin{(\omega t + \lambda)} \end{array}\right\}. \qquad \text{...(8.2)}$$

For an unloaded generator the currents $i_{d0}$ and $i_{q0}$ are both zero, and hence, from Eqns. (7.1):

$$e_{d0} = V_d = 0,$$
$$e_{q0} = V_q = -x_{md}i_f.$$

Thus the original phase voltage is:

$$e_{a0} = V_q \sin{(\omega t + \lambda)}.$$

The solution is best obtained by using the principle of super-position in the manner explained on page 67. The equations giving the changes in the currents are obtained by putting $e_f' = 0$, $e_d' = 0$, and $e_q' = -V_q 1$ in the equations for the super-imposed quantities corresponding to Eqns. (6.7):

$$\left.\begin{array}{l} 0 = p\psi_d' + \omega\psi_q' + r_a i_d \\ -V_q 1 = -\omega\psi_d' + p\psi_q' + r_a i_q \end{array}\right\}, \qquad \text{...(8.3)}$$

$i_d$ and $i_q$ have the same values as $i_d'$ and $i_q'$, because $i_{d0} = i_{q0} = 0$. The values of $\psi_d'$ and $\psi_q'$ are given by Eqns. (6.11) and (6.14), with $e_f = 0$. Hence Eqns. (8.3) become:

$$\left.\begin{array}{l} 0 = \left[ r_a + \dfrac{p}{\omega} x_d(p) \right] i_d + x_q(p) i_q \\ V_q 1 = x_d(p) i_d - \left[ r_a + \dfrac{p}{\omega} x_q(p) \right] i_q \end{array}\right\}. \qquad \text{...(8.4)}$$

*Solution for the short-circuit current*

Eliminating $i_q$ from Eqns. (8.4):

$$V_q 1 = \left[ p^2 + \omega^2 + p\omega r_a \left\{ \frac{1}{x_d(p)} + \frac{1}{x_q(p)} \right\} + \frac{\omega^2 r_a^2}{x_d(p)x_q(p)} \right] \frac{x_d(p)}{\omega^2} i_d.$$

$$\text{...(8.5)}$$

The expression in the square brackets can be simplified by making use of the fact that $r_a$ is small. The term in $r_a{}^2$ can be neglected entirely, and, in the term in $r_a$, $x_d(p)$ and $x_q(p)$ can be simplified by neglecting the resistances $r_f$, $r_{kd}$, $r_{kq}$. This is equivalent to replacing in this term all the factors of the form $(1+Tp)$ by $Tp$. With this approximation, $x_d(p)$ and $x_q(p)$ reduce to the subtransient reactances $x_d''$ and $x_q''$ (see page 123). Then

$$i_d = \frac{(1+T_{d0}'p)(1+T_{d0}''p)}{(1+T_d'p)(1+T_d''p)} \frac{\omega^2}{(p^2+2ap+\omega^2)} \frac{V_q \mathbf{1}}{x_d} \text{ (approx.), } \dots(8.6)$$

where $a = \dfrac{\omega r_a}{2}\left(\dfrac{1}{x_d''} + \dfrac{1}{x_q''}\right).$

The operational expression can be evaluated by the partial fraction method explained on page 46, if $(p^2+2ap+\omega^2)$ is factorised as $(p+a_1)(p+a_2)$.

$$i_d = \frac{V_q}{x_d}\left[ 1 - \frac{\left(1-\dfrac{T_{d0}'}{T_d'}\right)\left(1-\dfrac{T_{d0}''}{T_d'}\right)}{\left(1-\dfrac{T_d''}{T_d'}\right)\left(1-\dfrac{2a}{\omega^2 T_d'}+\dfrac{1}{\omega^2 T_d'^2}\right)}\varepsilon^{-t/T_d'} \right.$$

$$- \frac{\left(1-\dfrac{T_{d0}'}{T_d''}\right)\left(1-\dfrac{T_{d0}''}{T_d''}\right)}{\left(1-\dfrac{T_d'}{T_d''}\right)\left(1-\dfrac{2a}{\omega^2 T_d''}+\dfrac{1}{\omega^2 T_d''^2}\right)}\varepsilon^{-t/T_d''}$$

$$+ \frac{(1-a_1 T_{d0}')(1-a_1 T_{d0}'')}{(1-a_1 T_d')(1-a_1 T_d'')} \frac{\omega^2}{a_1(a_1-a_2)}\varepsilon^{-a_1 t}$$

$$\left. - \frac{(1-a_2 T_{d0}')(1-a_2 T_{d0}'')}{(1-a_2 T_d')(1-a_2 T_d'')} \frac{\omega^2}{a_2(a_1-a_2)}\varepsilon^{-a_2 t} \right]. \dots(8.7)$$

Now $T_d''$, $T_{d0}''$ are small compared with $T_d'$, $T_{d0}'$. In addition $T_{d0}'$, $T_{d0}''$, $T_d'$, $T_d''$ are all large compared with $1/\omega$, and $a$ is small compared with $\omega$. Hence

$$a_1 = a+j\omega \text{ (approx.),}$$
$$a_2 = a-j\omega \text{ (approx.),}$$

and

$$\frac{\omega^2}{(a_1-a_2)}\left(\frac{\varepsilon^{-a_1 t}}{a_1} - \frac{\varepsilon^{-a_2 t}}{a_2}\right) = -\varepsilon^{-at}\cos\omega t \text{ (approx.)}.$$

Hence, approximately, putting $a = 1/T_a$:

$$i_d = \frac{V_q}{x_d}\left[1 + \frac{(T_{d0}' - T_d')}{T_d'}\varepsilon^{-t/T_d'} + \frac{T_{d0}'}{T_d'}\frac{(T_{d0}'' - T_d'')}{T_d''}\varepsilon^{-t/T_d''}\right.$$

$$\left. - \frac{T_{d0}'T_{d0}''}{T_d'T_d''}\varepsilon^{-t/T_a}\cos\omega t\right]$$

$$= \frac{V_q}{x_d} + \left(\frac{V_q}{x_d'} - \frac{V_q}{x_d}\right)\varepsilon^{-t/T_d'} + \left(\frac{V_q}{x_d''} - \frac{V_q}{x_d'}\right)\varepsilon^{-t/T_d''}$$

$$- \frac{V_q}{x_d''}\varepsilon^{-t/T_a}\cos\omega t. \qquad \ldots(8.8)$$

The quadrature current $i_q$ may be found in a similar way.

$$i_q = -\frac{(1 + T_{q0}''p)}{(1 + T_q''p)}\frac{p\omega}{(p^2 + 2ap + \omega^2)}\frac{V_q 1}{x_q}$$

$$= -\frac{V_q}{x_q''}\varepsilon^{-t/T_a}\sin\omega t \text{ (approx.)}. \qquad \ldots(8.9)$$

$x_d'$ is the transient reactance the value of which is given on page 123.

Substitution of the values of $i_d$ and $i_q$ in the transformation equations (6.4) with $\theta = (\omega t + \lambda)$ gives the expressions for $i_a$, $i_b$ and $i_c$:

$$i_a = \left[\frac{V_q}{x_d} + \left(\frac{V_q}{x_d'} - \frac{V_q}{x_d}\right)\varepsilon^{-t/T_d'} + \left(\frac{V_q}{x_d''} - \frac{V_q}{x_d'}\right)\varepsilon^{-t/T_d''}\right]\cos(\omega t + \lambda)$$

$$- \frac{V_q}{x_m}\varepsilon^{-t/T_a}\cos\lambda - \frac{V_q}{x_n}\varepsilon^{-t/T_a}\cos(2\omega t + \lambda), \qquad \ldots(8.10)$$

where $x_m = \dfrac{2x_d''x_q''}{x_d'' + x_q''}$,

$$x_n = \frac{2x_d''x_q''}{x_q'' - x_d''}.$$

The values of $i_b$ and $i_c$ are obtained by replacing $\lambda$ by $(\lambda-2\pi/3)$ and $(\lambda-4\pi/3)$ respectively in the expression for $i_a$. The values of $x_d$, $x_d'$, $x_d''$ and $x_q''$ are given on page 123.

## The short-circuit torque

In order to find an expression for the torque, it is necessary to determine the quantities $\psi_d$ and $\psi_q$. Before the short circuit the values are, from Eqns. (6.7):

$$\psi_{d0}=-\frac{V_q}{\omega},$$

$$\psi_{q0}=0.$$

After the short circuit the values are:

$$\psi_d=\psi_{d0}+\psi_d',$$
$$\psi_q=\psi_{q0}+\psi_q',$$

where $\psi_d'$, $\psi_q'$ are the superimposed quantities obtained from Eqns. (8.3), (6.11) and (6.14). Using Eqn. (8.6):

$$\psi_d'=\frac{x_d(p)}{\omega}i_d=\frac{\omega}{p^2+2ap+\omega^2}V_q\mathbf{1}$$

$$=\frac{V_q}{\omega}(1-\varepsilon^{-t/T_a}\cos \omega t).$$

Hence

$$\psi_d=-\frac{V_q}{\omega}\varepsilon^{-t/T_a}\cos \omega t. \qquad \ldots(8.11)$$

Similarly

$$\psi_q=-\frac{V_q}{\omega}\varepsilon^{-t/T_a}\sin \omega t. \qquad \ldots(8.12)$$

The two flux waves represented by $\psi_d$ and $\psi_q$ combine to form a forward rotating flux wave, which rotates at speed $\omega$ and is therefore stationary relative to the armature. Its magnitude dies away with the armature time constant $T_a$, which depends on the armature resistance. Thus the effect of the short circuit can be explained by imagining that the flux, which rotates relatively to the armature during normal operation, is frozen in position relative to the armature at the instant of short circuit, and then dies away with time constant $T_a$.

The torque is obtained by substituting the expressions for $\psi_d$, $\psi_q$, $i_d$, $i_q$ in Eqn. (6.8).

$$f_e = \frac{V_q{}^2}{2}\left[\varepsilon^{-t/T_a}\cos\omega t\left\{\frac{1}{x_q{}''}\varepsilon^{-t/T_a}\sin\omega t\right\}\right.$$
$$+\varepsilon^{-t/T_a}\sin\omega t\left\{\frac{1}{x_d}+\left(\frac{1}{x_d{}'}-\frac{1}{x_d}\right)\varepsilon^{-t/T_d'}+\left(\frac{1}{x_d{}''}-\frac{1}{x_d{}'}\right)\varepsilon^{-t/T_d''}\right.$$
$$\left.\left.-\frac{1}{x_d{}''}\varepsilon^{-t/T_a}\cos\omega t\right\}\right]$$
$$=E^2\varepsilon^{-t/T_a}\sin\omega t\left\{\frac{1}{x_d}+\left(\frac{1}{x_d{}'}-\frac{1}{x_d}\right)\varepsilon^{-t/T_d'}+\left(\frac{1}{x_d{}''}-\frac{1}{x_d{}'}\right)\varepsilon^{-t/T_d''}\right\}$$
$$+\frac{E^2}{2}\varepsilon^{-2t/T_a}\sin 2\omega t\left(\frac{1}{x_q{}''}-\frac{1}{x_d{}''}\right), \quad \ldots(8.13)$$

where $E$ is the R.M.S. voltage equal to $V_q/\sqrt{2}$.

The double frequency torque represented by the second term of Eqns. (8.13) is relatively small. Hence the principal component of torque oscillates at normal frequency and has an initial amplitude $E^2/x_d{}''$.

*The field current after the short circuit*

The field current before the short circuit is given by Eqns. (7.1), with $i_d = i_q = 0$.

$$i_{f0} = -\frac{e_{q0}}{x_{md}} = -\frac{V_q}{x_{md}}.$$

The field current after the short circuit is obtained by adding to $i_{f0}$ the superimposed current $i_f'$ determined by solving the equations already used to calculate the armature current. A relation between $i_f'$ and $i_d$ can be obtained by eliminating $i_{kd}$ from the second and third Eqns. (6.17), with $e_f = 0$.

$$[\{r_f+(L_{md}+l_f)p\}\{r_{kd}+(L_{md}+l_{kd})p\}-L_{md}{}^2p^2]i_f'$$
$$+L_{md}p(r_{kd}+l_{kd}p)i_d=0.$$

Hence, substituting the value of $i_d$ from Eqn. (8.6):

$$i_f' = -\frac{L_{md}p(1+T_{kd}p)}{r_f(1+T_{d0}'p)(1+T_{d0}''p)}\,i_d$$
$$= -\frac{(1+T_{kd}p)}{(1+T_d'p)(1+T_d''p)}\frac{\omega p}{(p^2+2ap+\omega^2)}\frac{x_{md}}{x_d}\frac{V_q}{r_f}1. \quad \ldots(8.14)$$

The following operational solution is obtained by using the partial fraction method and making the same approximations as on page 147.

$$i_f' = -\frac{V_q x_{md}}{\omega T_d' r_f x_d}\left[\varepsilon^{-t/T_d'} - \left(1 - \frac{T_{kd}}{T_d''}\right)\varepsilon^{-t/T_d''} - \frac{T_{kd}}{T_d''}\varepsilon^{-t/T_a}\cos\omega t\right].$$

Now

$$-\frac{V_q x_{md}}{\omega T_d' r_f x_d} = \frac{i_{f0}}{T_d'}\frac{x_{md}^2}{\omega r_f x_d} = i_{f0}\frac{T_{d0}' - T_d'}{T_d'} = i_{f0}\frac{x_d - x_d'}{x_d'}.$$

Hence the total field current after the short circuit is given by:

$$i_f = i_{f0} + i_f'$$

$$= i_{f0} + i_{f0}\left(\frac{x_d - x_d'}{x_d'}\right)\left[\varepsilon^{-t/T_d'} - \left(1 - \frac{T_{kd}}{T_d''}\right)\varepsilon^{-t/T_d''},\right.$$

$$\left. - \frac{T_{kd}}{T_d''}\varepsilon^{-t/T_a}\cos\omega t\right]. \quad \ldots(8.15)$$

### 33. The Analysis of Short-circuit Oscillograms

*Oscillograms of armature currents*

As already mentioned, a sudden short-circuit test, taken by short circuiting simultaneously the three phases of an alternator when running unloaded at normal voltage, is an accepted method of checking its transient characteristics. From the oscillograms of the armature currents the principal transient reactances and time constants can be calculated.

Fig. 47 shows the curves of armature current after a short circuit on a 30,000-kVA. synchronous condenser. The curves agree very closely with the expression for the current in phase $A$ given in Eqn. (8.10) and the corresponding expressions for the currents in phases $B$ and $C$.

In Fig. 47 envelope lines are drawn through the peaks of the alternating current waves, and dotted lines are drawn half-way between the envelope curves. Thus the current can be divided into a unidirectional or *asymmetrical component*, and an *alternating component* of supply frequency. Both components start with a certain *initial value* and become less as time proceeds. The initial values of the alternating components are determined by producing the envelope curves back to zero time.

The dotted lines give the asymmetrical currents expressed by the fourth term of Eqn. (8.10) and by the fourth terms of the corresponding expressions for $i_b$ and $i_c$. The initial values are different in the three phases $A$, $B$ and $C$, being proportional to $\cos \lambda$, $\cos (\lambda - 2\pi/3)$ and $\cos (\lambda - 4\pi/3)$ respectively, but the three currents all die away to zero with the same time constant $T_a$.

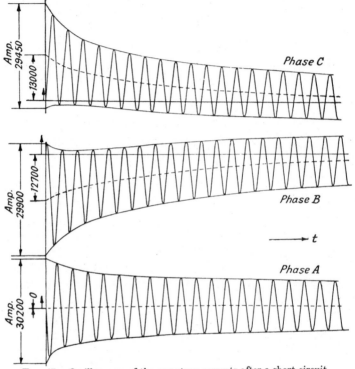

FIG. 47.—Oscillograms of the armature currents after a short circuit.

By replotting the dotted curves on semi-log paper (see Ref. 33.1) the reactance $x_m$, the angle $\lambda$, and the time constant $T_a$, can be accurately determined.

The alternating component for any phase remains after deducting the asymmetrical component from the appropriate curve in Fig. 47. There is a small second harmonic component corresponding to the last term of Eqn. (8.11), but it is in most cases negligible because it depends on the difference of the two subtransient reactances. Because the rate at which the amplitude of the alternating component decreases is slow in relation to the fundamental A.C. cycle, a curve showing the variation of the R.M.S. value with time can be plotted. Such a curve, shown as a full line in Fig. 48, is obtained by measuring the intercepts between the envelope lines in Fig. 47.

The ordinate of the curve $AB$ in Fig. 48, which shows the per-unit value of R.M.S. current at any time, is proportional to the expression in square brackets in Eqn. (8.10). Although the

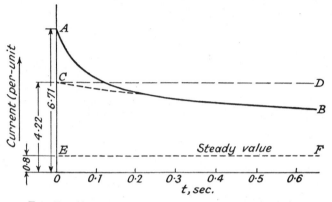

FIG. 48.—Alternating component of the short-circuit current.

phase of the alternating wave depends on $\lambda$ and differs in the three phases in accordance with the cosine term outside the brackets, the R.M.S. value is the same in all phases. The initial value, obtained by putting $t=0$, is $V_q/x_d''$. As time passes the current decreases, first rapidly and then more slowly, and finally settles down to a steady value.

The current given by the curve $AB$ in Fig. 48 can be further subdivided into three parts, corresponding to the three terms inside the square brackets in Eqn. (8.10). The steady short-circuit current, indicated by the dotted line $EF$, is $V_q/x_d$. The *transient component*, shown by the dotted line $CB$, has an initial value $EC=V_q/x_d'-V_q/x_d$, and dies away with time constant $T_d'$. The *subtransient component*, given by the intercept between $AB$ and $CB$, has an initial value $CA=V_q/x_d'' -V_q/x_d'$, and dies away with time constant $T_d''$. The five components of the short-circuit current are listed in Table 2.

TABLE 2

COMPONENTS OF THE SHORT-CIRCUIT CURRENT

| Component | Initial Value | Frequency | Time Constant |
|---|---|---|---|
| *Alternating components* Steady .. .. .. | $\dfrac{V_q}{x_d}$ | Fundamental | — |
| Transient .. .. | $\dfrac{V_q}{x_d{}'} - \dfrac{V_q}{x_d}$ | Fundamental | $T_d{}'$ |
| Subtransient .. .. | $\dfrac{V_q}{x_d{}''} - \dfrac{V_q}{x_d{}'}$ | Fundamental | $T_d{}''$ |
| *Other components* Asymmetrical .. .. | $\dfrac{V_q}{x_m} \cos \lambda$ | Zero | $T_a$ |
| Second harmonic .. | $\dfrac{V_q}{x_n}$ | Double fundamental | $T_a$ |

Thus the values of the direct-axis transient and subtransient reactances and time constants can be deduced from the short-circuit oscillograms. The analysis of the short-circuit oscillogram brings out the physical meaning of the subtransient and transient reactances. The subtransient reactance $x_d{}''$ is the effective reactance of the generator determining the initial value of the alternating component of the short-circuit current. The transient reactance $x_d{}'$ is the effective reactance determining the initial current which would flow if the rapidly decaying subtransient component were not present.

Figs. 47 and 48 are taken from Ref. 51.7, in which the results of a numerical check are given.

*Oscillogram of field current*

Fig. 49 shows the oscillogram of the field current taken at the same time as the armature current curves of Fig. 47. Envelope lines are drawn as before, and a dotted line is drawn half-way between the envelope lines. The total current is thus shown to consist of a unidirectional component given by the dotted line, and an alternating component.

The alternating component corresponds to the last term of Eqn. (8.15). It is of fundamental frequency and dies away with time constant $T_a$. The unidirectional component starts with the steady value $i_{f0}$, rises suddenly at the instant of short

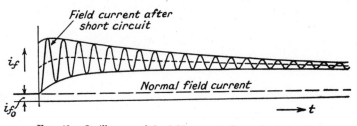

FIG. 49.—Oscillogram of the field current after a short circuit.

circuit and follows the dotted curve until it finally returns to the steady value. This component corresponds to the first three terms of Eqn. (8.15).

The dotted curve of Fig. 49 derived from the oscillogram is

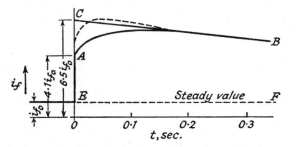

FIG. 50.—Unidirectional component of the field current.

replotted as the dotted curve in Fig. 50. Fig. 50 shows also the curve $AB$ calculated from the first three terms of Eqn. (8.15), and the curve $CB$ corresponding to the first two terms. The unidirectional field current given by the curve $AB$ may be built up from three parts:

1. Steady field current $i_{f0}$ given by the line $EF$.
2. Transient component given by the intercept between $EF$ and $CB$. This part dies away with time constant $T_d'$.

155

3. Subtransient component given by the intercept between $CB$ and $AB$. This part is deducted from the curve $CB$ and dies away with time constant $T_d''$.

The agreement between test and calculation is not as good as for the armature current since the subtransient component for the dotted curve is smaller and dies away more rapidly than the calculated value. The reason is probably that there are other closed damping paths, not allowed for in the theory, in which current can flow so as to modify the field current. It may be noted that the value of $OC$ is $i_{f0}\dfrac{x_d}{x_d'}$. This gives an indication of the rise in field current, but the peak current is actually greater because the oscillating component must be added to the curve $CB$.

The four components of the field current correspond quite closely to the four components of the direct-axis current $i_d$ in Eqn. (8.8), both as regards the time constant of decay and whether the component is unidirectional or alternating. They also correspond to the components of the phase current $i_a$ in Eqn. (8.10), but in this case a unidirectional component in the field current corresponds to an alternating component in the armature current and vice versa. In each case the corresponding components in the windings produce M.M.F.s of the same type; for example, the unidirectional field and the alternating armature current both produce M.M.F.s that are stationary relative to the field. The magnitudes of corresponding components differ, however, because of the current in the quadrature-axis damping winding, and because of the M.M.F. required to magnetise the core.

**34. Short Circuit or Sudden Change of Voltage on a Loaded Alternator**

For an alternator which is short-circuited when it is operating on load, the same equations apply as for an unloaded machine, but the steady values of voltage and current before the short circuit are different. The axis voltages $e_{d0}$ and $e_{q0}$ are given by Eqns. (7.1), and for a normal loaded condition $e_{d0}$ is not zero. As on page 146, the symbols $V_d$ and $V_q$ are used to distinguish these steady voltages before the short circuit.

The method of superposition can be used as before to determine the change of current resulting from the sudden application of voltages $-V_d$ and $-V_q$. The appropriate equations are therefore:

$$-V_d\mathbf{1}=p\psi_d'+\omega\psi_q'+r_a i_d' \\ -V_q\mathbf{1}=-\omega\psi_d'+p\psi_q'+r_a i_q' \Bigg\} . \qquad ...(8.16)$$

The total short-circuit current $i_a$ is obtained by adding the current determined from these equations to the original current $i_{a0}$, and is thus the sum of three quantities:

1. The original steady current $i_{a0}$.
2. The current $i_{a1}$ obtained by solving Eqns. (8.16) with $V_d=0$. The expression for $i_{a1}$ is given by Eqn. (8.10).
3. The current $i_{a2}$ obtained by solving Eqns. (8.16) with $V_q=0$. The expression for $i_{a2}$ is similar to that in Eqn. (8.10) except that it contains the quadrature-axis reactances and time constants instead of those for the direct axis. The components correspond to those of $i_{a1}$, except that there is no transient component because there is no field winding on the quadrature axis.

$$i_{a2}=-\left[\frac{V_d}{x_q}+\left(\frac{V_d}{x_q''}-\frac{V_d}{x_q}\right)\varepsilon^{-t/T_q''}\right]\sin(\omega t+\lambda)$$
$$+\frac{V_d}{x_m}\varepsilon^{-t/T_a}\sin\lambda-\frac{V_d}{x_n}\varepsilon^{-t/T_a}\sin(2\omega t+\lambda). \quad ...(8.17)$$

Thus the theory explained in Sect. 32 can be used to obtain a complete solution for the current following a sudden three-phase short circuit from any condition of steady operation. The field current $i_f$ and the flux linkages $\psi_d$ and $\psi_q$ can also be determined in a similar way, using the principle of superposition. The torque can be calculated by substituting the complete expressions for $i_d$, $i_q$, $\psi_d$, $\psi_q$ in Eqn. (6.8).

*Sudden change of voltage*

The method just explained can also be used to calculate the change of current if the generator, instead of being short-circuited, is suddenly switched over to a different voltage, obtained from an 'infinite bus' synchronised with the generator and unaffected by the current. $V_d$ and $V_q$ must now be the amounts by which the direct and quadrature axis voltages are reduced. The total current is calculated as before by adding the two currents deduced from these voltages to the original current.

### The effect of series impedance

If an external impedance, consisting of a resistance $r_e$ and reactance $x_e$, is in series with the generator both before and after the short circuit or sudden change of voltage, the equations still hold, provided that the external impedance is added to the internal impedance of the generator. Hence the results can be used, if $r_a$ and $x_a$ are replaced by $r_t$ and $x_t$, where

$$\left. \begin{array}{l} r_t = r_a + r_e \\ x_t = x_a + r_e \end{array} \right\} . \qquad \qquad ...(8.18)$$

All the reactances and time constants are modified by the increase of armature impedance. Since many of the approximations depend on the assumption that $r_a$ is small, the accuracy is reduced by the introduction of $r_e$. If $r_e$ is large, it may be necessary to make a more laborious calculation in which the approximations are not made.

# CHAPTER IX

## *Synchronising Phenomena and Sustained Oscillations in Synchronous Machines*

### 35. General Equations for Operation near to Synchronous Speed

In the present chapter certain problems are considered for which the speed of the machine is not constant. The general equations are then non-linear, as explained in connection with Items 5, 6 and 7 of Table 1, page 36. Sect. 36 discusses the problem of synchronising a synchronous motor, while Sects. 37 and 38 deal with small oscillations in synchronous machines. In both of these examples the armature winding is connected to a balanced three-phase supply, and the speed is near to synchronous speed. The equations can then be rearranged as shown below.

The method introduces the angle $\delta$ by which the rotor position lags behind the position it would have during synchronous operation at no load. In order to understand the physical meaning of the angle $\delta$ it is necessary to visualise in Fig. 3 an imaginary reference axis, rotating at synchronous speed $\omega$ and occupying the position that phase $A$ would have if the machine ran steadily with the armature winding connected to the supply voltage but with no current in it. Under steady conditions $\delta$ is the constant load angle defined on page 97. Its value is positive for motoring, negative for generating, and zero for no-load operation. For a motor before it is synchronised $\delta$ is a variable angle, which is positive at first and settles down to a constant value as the motor pulls into synchronism. In the hunting problems considered in Sects. 37 and 38, $\delta$ oscillates about a mean value.

The position $\theta_r$ of the reference axis at any instant is given by

$$\theta_r = \omega t,$$

and with a varying speed the machine position is

$$\theta = \omega t - \delta. \qquad \qquad ...(9.1)$$

159

The phase voltage $e_a$ can be expressed as

$$e_a = E_m \sin \omega t$$
$$= E_m \sin (\theta + \delta)$$
$$= E_m \sin \delta \cos \theta + E_m \cos \delta \sin \theta.$$

Comparing this with the transformation equation (6.2), with $e_0 = 0$, and equating coefficients:

$$e_d = E_m \sin \delta,$$
$$e_q = E_m \cos \delta.$$

The speed is obtained by differentiating Eqn. (9.1):

$$v = \omega - p\delta.$$

Hence, substituting these values in Eqns. (6.7), the modified general equations are obtained.

$$\left. \begin{array}{l} E_m \sin \delta = p\psi_d + \omega\psi_q + r_a i_d - \psi_q \cdot p\delta \\ E_m \cos \delta = -\omega\psi_d + p\psi_q + r_a i_q + \psi_d \cdot p\delta \end{array} \right\} . \qquad \ldots(9.2)$$

From Eqn. (9.1) the acceleration is:

$$\frac{d^2\theta}{dt^2} = -p^2\delta.$$

Hence the torque equation is:

$$f_t = \frac{\omega}{2}(\psi_d i_q - \psi_q i_d) - \frac{2H}{\omega}p^2\delta. \qquad \ldots(9.3)$$

### 36. The Synchronising Problem

The term *synchronising* applies to the operating condition when two or more synchronous machines pull into synchronism with each other after they have been running at different speeds. It occurs most frequently when a motor or generator, which is to operate with a supply system connected to other synchronous machines, is being started up, or after a disturbance has caused it temporarily to lose synchronism. This section contains a brief discussion, based on Ref. 35.3, of the problem of synchronising a synchronous motor after it has run up as an induction motor to a speed just below synchronous speed. The problem is of the fifth type listed in Table 1, page 36, since the speed is an unknown function of time. The equations for the currents and the speed are non-linear differential equations, and cannot be solved by any exact mathematical

160

method. For the investigation recorded in Ref. 35.3, a mechanical differential analyser was used to obtain numerical solutions of several alternative conditions.

*Application of the differential analyser*

In order to use a differential analyser of the type described on page 51, Eqns. (9.2), (9.3), (6.11), (6.14), (6.22), (6.23) and (6.25) must be rearranged so that each term can be represented by the angular position of a shaft on the analyser. When the shafts representing the terms of any equation are suitably coupled by means of 'adder' elements, the quantities must satisfy that equation. The expression for $\psi_d$ can be put into partial fractions of the form:

$$\psi_d = \frac{x_d i_d}{\omega} + \frac{A_1 i_d + B_1 e_f}{1 + T_{do}' p} + \frac{A_2 i_d + B_2 e_f}{1 + T_{do}'' p}$$
$$= \frac{x_d i_d}{\omega} + \psi_{d1} + \psi_{d2}, \qquad \ldots(9.4)$$

where $A_1$, $B_1$, $A_2$, $B_2$ are constant quantities depending on the machine constants, and $\psi_{d1}$, $\psi_{d2}$ are new variables introduced to assist in obtaining the solution.

The applied torque is the load torque $F$, and is negative because power is taken from the motor.

$$f_t = -F. \qquad \ldots(9.5)$$

Hence the following seven equations, containing the seven dependent variables $\delta$, $i_d$, $i_q$, $\psi_d$, $\psi_{d1}$, $\psi_{d2}$ and $\psi_q$, and the independent variable $t$, are obtained.

$$
\left.
\begin{aligned}
E_m \sin \delta &= p\psi_d + \omega\psi_q + r_a i_d - \psi_q p\delta \\
E_m \cos \delta &= -\omega\psi_d + p\psi_q + r_a i_q + \psi_d p\delta \\
\psi_d &= \frac{x_d i_d}{\omega} + \psi_{d1} + \psi_{d2} \\
\psi_{d1} + T_{do}' p\psi_{d1} &= A_1 i_d + B_1 e_f \\
\psi_{d2} + T_{do}'' p\psi_{d2} &= A_2 i_d + B_2 e_f \\
\psi_q + T_{qo}'' p\psi_q &= \frac{x_q}{\omega} i_q + \frac{x_q T_q''}{\omega} p i_q \\
\frac{4H}{\omega^2} p\delta &= \frac{2F}{\omega} t + \int \psi_d i_q dt - \int \psi_q i_d dt
\end{aligned}
\right\} \qquad \ldots(9.6)
$$

On the differential analyser, shafts may first be allocated to the variables $t$, $p\delta$, $i_d$, $pi_q$, $p\psi_d$, $p\psi_{d1}$, $p\psi_{d2}$, $p\psi_q$ and the known voltage $e_f$.

It is then possible, by means of 'integrator' elements, to derive the quantities

$$\delta,\ i_q,\ \psi_d,\ \psi_{d1},\ \psi_{d2},\ \psi_q,\ \int\psi_d i_q dt,\ \text{and}\ \int\psi_q i_d dt.$$

The integral of a product is obtained by two successive integrations; for example:

$$\int\psi_d i_q dt = \int\psi_d d(\int i_q dt).$$

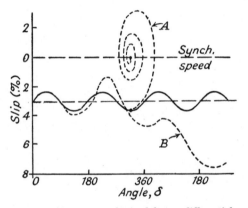

Fig. 51.—Synchronising curves obtained from a differential analyser.

The terms $E_m \sin \delta$ and $E_m \cos \delta$ are obtained from 'function tables', and $\psi_d p\delta$ and $\psi_q p\delta$ come from 'multiplier' elements. Any quantity can be multiplied by a coefficient by means of a 'constant multiplier' element.

Thus the differential analyser can be set up so that the variables satisfy the equations. It must be brought into action with the correct initial conditions, and can then be used to determine the currents and the angle as functions of time.

Fig. 51 shows a typical result selected from those given in Ref. 35.3, to which reference should be made for fuller details. In this diagram the slip, derived as $p\delta$, is plotted as a function of the angle $\delta$. The curves are obtained in two stages. The full line, showing the periodic curve obtained before the synchronising switch is closed, is determined by a preliminary run on the analyser, taken with $e_f = 0$. The synchronising curve, shown by a dotted line, depends on the instant at which the switch is closed. Two alternative curves, marked $A$ and $B$, determined by means of the differential analyser with the appropriate initial conditions, are shown on Fig. 51. For one instant of switching (curve $A$) the speed rises to synchronous speed, and then after some oscillation settles down to steady synchronous operation. For another less favourable instant (curve $B$) the machine does not pull into step, but would settle down to another condition of continuous oscillation.

### 37. Forced Oscillations and Free Oscillations

Under certain conditions a synchronous machine, connected to a supply system and otherwise operating normally at synchronous speed, may oscillate in speed about the mean value. When this occurs the currents in all the windings also pulsate at the same frequency, which is usually much lower than the frequency of the A.C. supply. The rotor of the machine, instead of running exactly in synchronism at a constant angle $\delta$ ahead of or behind the no-load reference axis, oscillates about a mean position. The oscillations may be *forced oscillations* caused by pulsating torques originating outside the machine, or *free oscillations* arising in the machine itself by a process of self-excitation.

Forced oscillations occur in alternators driven by diesel engines or in synchronous motors driving reciprocating compressors. Engines and compressors are usually built with several cylinders in order to reduce the magnitude of the torque pulsations. The torque diagram can be analysed into harmonic torques of many different frequencies so that the effect of each can be calculated independently. The higher harmonics are too rapid to affect the flux and current in the machine appreciably, and their analysis becomes a purely mechanical problem depending on the stiffness of the shaft. On the other hand, the slowest torque pulsations, occurring once per revolution, or once per two revolutions in a four-stroke engine, and arising due to unbalance between cylinders, may cause serious pulsations of the current. For such slow oscillations the shaft can usually be assumed to be perfectly stiff. The maximum value of the angular pulsation in electrical degrees is known as the *angular deviation*.

Free oscillations, or *hunting*, on the other hand, occur without any externally applied torque pulsations. For example, a small synchronous motor, having a relatively high armature resistance and a weak damper winding, may oscillate continuously when connected to an A.C. supply system.

The analysis of small oscillations in a synchronous machine is carried out by considering an equivalent mechanical system having stiffness and damping. As a starting-point, suppose that the angular position of the armature, defined by the angle $\delta$, oscillates sinusoidally about its mean value. The electrical torque developed by the machine also pulsates at the same frequency about its mean value, and if the oscillations are so small that product terms in the equations can be neglected, the torque pulsation is sinusoidal as well, and its magnitude is proportional to the magnitude of the angular pulsation. The torque pulsation is, however, not necessarily in phase with the angular pulsation, but can be resolved into two components, one in phase and one in quadrature. The component of the torque pulsation which is in phase with the angular pulsation is equivalent to the *elastic torque* of a spring, while the quadrature component, which is in phase with the pulsation of angular velocity, is equivalent to the *damping torque* of a viscous damper. Thus the values of the *elastic constant*, or stiffness, and of the *damping constant* of the equivalent mechanical system can be found.

It should be noted that the values of the elastic and damping constants so found only apply at one frequency, and are not constant at all frequencies as in the spring or damper of a mechanical system. However, the values at different frequencies can be plotted on a curve and used to calculate the pulsations at any frequency.

*Analysis of the mechanical system*

The synchronous machine is analogous to a simple mechanical system having stiffness, damping and inertia. The equations of such a system can be written down either for any general motion or for a small oscillation. In order to put the equation in a form which can be applied to an electrical machine, the quantities are expressed on a per-unit basis.

Let $\theta$ be the angle of displacement from the unstrained position, in radians,

$f$ be the instantaneous externally applied torque,

$K$ be the elastic constant, expressed as torque per radian,

$C$ be the damping constant, expressed as torque per radian per second.

The angle of displacement in the mechanical system corresponds to the load angle $\delta$ of the machine measured in electrical radians. The appropriate value of the inertia coefficient is that given on page 33, and hence the accelerating torque is $\dfrac{2H}{\omega}p^2\theta$. The torques due to stiffness and damping are $K\theta$ and $Cp\theta$ respectively, and the differential equation is:

$$\frac{2H}{\omega}p^2\theta + Cp\theta + K\theta = f. \qquad \ldots(9.7)$$

For a small oscillation at frequency $m/2\pi$ the equation for the complex numbers $\Delta\Theta$ and $\Delta\mathbf{F}$ representing the angle and torque pulsations is:

$$-m^2\frac{2H}{\omega}\Delta\Theta + jmC\Delta\Theta + K\Delta\Theta = \Delta\mathbf{F}. \qquad \ldots(9.8)$$

Hence the angular pulsation is given by:

$$\Delta\Theta = \frac{\Delta\mathbf{F}}{\left(K - \dfrac{2m^2H}{\omega}\right) + jmC}. \qquad \ldots(9.9)$$

In a simple mechanical system with viscous damping, $K$ and $C$ are constants. Eqn. (9.9) shows how the angular pulsation varies with frequency in both magnitude and phase, assuming a given value of torque pulsation. If there were no damping the angular pulsation would become infinite when $K = \dfrac{2m^2H}{\omega}$.

The frequency at which this occurs is called the *natural frequency* and is given by:

$$\frac{m_0}{2\pi} = \frac{1}{2\pi}\sqrt{\frac{K\omega}{2H}}. \qquad \text{...(9.10)}$$

When damping is present, the maximum oscillation is limited by the value of $C$ and occurs at a frequency close to the natural frequency, if $C$ is small.

*Approximate method for forced oscillations in an electrical system (old method)*

A simple method of determining the angular deviation of a synchronous machine due to an applied torque pulsation has been in use for many years (see Ref. 27.1). The method depends on the conception of the machine as an undamped torsional spring in which the restoring torque varies with the angular displacement $\delta$, in the manner shown in the curve of Fig. 38. For an oscillation superimposed on a given steady load, the appropriate value for the spring constant is $P_0$, the slope of the power angle curve at that load, since torque and power are equal on the per-unit system. A formula for $P_0$, obtained by neglecting the armature resistance, is given in Eqn. (5.10).

The simplified method thus takes $K=P_0$ and $C=0$. With these assumptions the machine has a natural frequency, at which the oscillation would become very large, given by:

$$\frac{m_0}{2\pi} = \frac{1}{2\pi}\sqrt{\frac{P_0\omega}{2H}}. \qquad \text{...(9.11)}$$

If there is no damping, it is important that the frequency of the forced oscillation shall not coincide with the natural frequency. For a frequency differing appreciably from the natural frequency the angular deviation may be calculated, using Eqn. (9.10), with $C=0$.

When the natural frequency of a synchronous machine calculated by the above method is too close to the frequency of the applied torque, there are two ways of overcoming the difficulty. One is to increase the moment of inertia so as to lower the natural frequency, and the other is to introduce a large amount of damping. Modern practice favours the second method, which is carried out by fitting a heavy damper winding arranged so as to be effective on both the direct and quadrature axes.

For a machine with no damper winding the simplified method is approximately correct because the damping effect of the closed field winding is small. When, however, there is appreciable damping, whether due to a squirrel-cage winding or to eddy current paths in solid iron, the method may be very misleading. The damper winding not only introduces the damping constant $C$, which is neglected in the simplified method, but also causes the spring constant $K$ to differ considerably from $P_0$. Both $K$ and $C$ vary with the frequency of the oscillation, and the natural frequency calculated from Eqn. (9.11) becomes meaningless. The values of the constants can be calculated accurately by the method given in Sect. 38.

*Criterion for free oscillations*

For a self-excited free oscillation to occur when there is no external torque pulsation, $\Delta\Theta$ in Eqn. (9.9) must have a value even when $\Delta\mathbf{F}$ is zero. Hence the denominator of Eqn. (9.9) must be zero. Separating out real and imaginary parts:

$$\left. \begin{array}{r} K - \dfrac{2H}{\omega}m^2 = 0 \\ C = 0 \end{array} \right\}. \qquad (9.12)$$

If $C$ were negative, the condition would be unstable, causing an oscillation which would increase in magnitude indefinitely. In practice the machine saturates and the oscillation is limited, but the magnitude attained under this condition may become very large and cause serious trouble. The criterion that determines whether self-excitation can occur is that the value of $C$, calculated from the theory of small oscillations, shall be zero or negative; in other words, that there shall be *negative damping*.

Now $K$ and $C$ are both functions of $m$. Hence the condition for self-excitation is that $C$ shall be zero or negative at the frequency for which $K = \dfrac{2H}{\omega}m^2$. The problem is discussed further in Sect. 38.

167

## 38. Calculation of the Elastic and Damping Constants

In the following analysis the notation is the same as that used on page 66. The steady values about which the oscillations occur are indicated by the suffix 0; for example, the direct-axis steady current is $i_{d0}$. The complex numbers representing the small oscillations are denoted by a capital letter with the prefix $\Delta$; for example, the pulsation of the direct-axis current is $\Delta\mathbf{I}_d$. (The small letter is used in the symbol $\Delta\mathbf{\delta}$.)

In order to compare the synchronous machine with the mechanical system discussed on page 165, the torque must be taken as positive when the machine acts as a motor, since a positive torque then acts so as to reduce the positive angle $\delta$, as assumed for the spring. With this convention, the torque $f$ is equal and opposite to the electrical torque $f_e$, defined on page 31, or

$$f = -f_e.$$

*Equations for steady operation*

The equations for steady operation are obtained by putting $p=0$ in Eqns. (9.2), (6.8), (6.11) and (6.14).

$$E_m \sin \delta_0 = \omega\psi_{q0} + r_a i_{d0}. \qquad \ldots(9.13)$$

$$E_m \cos \delta_0 = -\omega\psi_{d0} + r_a i_{q0}. \qquad \ldots(9.14)$$

$$\omega\psi_{d0} = x_d i_{d0} + \frac{x_{md}}{r_f} e_{f0}. \qquad \ldots(9.15)$$

$$\omega\psi_{q0} = x_q i_{q0}. \qquad \ldots(9.16)$$

$$f_0 = -f_{e0} = \frac{\omega}{2}(\psi_{d0} i_{q0} - \psi_{q0} i_{d0}). \qquad \ldots(9.17)$$

*Equations for small oscillations*

The equations for small oscillations at frequency $m/2\pi$ are derived from the same equations by the method explained in Sect. 12, putting $p=jm$. Since the field voltage is constant, $\Delta\mathbf{E}_f = 0$.

$$E_m \cos \delta_0 \Delta\mathbf{\delta} = jm\Delta\mathbf{\Psi}_d + \omega\Delta\mathbf{\Psi}_q + r_a\Delta\mathbf{I}_d - jm\psi_{q0}\Delta\mathbf{\delta}. \qquad \ldots(9.18)$$

$$-E_m \sin \delta_0 \varDelta\boldsymbol\delta = -\omega\varDelta\boldsymbol\Psi_d + jm\varDelta\boldsymbol\Psi_q + r_a\varDelta\mathbf{I}_q + jm\psi_{d0}\varDelta\boldsymbol\delta.$$

$$\dots(9.19)$$

$$\omega\varDelta\boldsymbol\Psi_d = x_d(jm)\varDelta\mathbf{I}_d. \qquad \dots(9.20)$$

$$\omega\varDelta\boldsymbol\Psi_q = x_q(jm)\varDelta\mathbf{I}_q. \qquad \dots(9.21)$$

$$\varDelta\mathbf{F} = -\varDelta\mathbf{F}_e = -\frac{\omega}{2}(i_{q0}\varDelta\boldsymbol\Psi_d + \psi_{d0}\varDelta\mathbf{I}_q - i_{d0}\varDelta\boldsymbol\Psi_q - \psi_{q0}\varDelta\mathbf{I}_d).$$

$$\dots(9.22)$$

*Approximate method for forced oscillations (new method)*

A simple approximate formula for the elastic and damping constants can be derived by neglecting the armature resistance $r_a$, as was done in obtaining the expressions for $P$ and $P_0$ in Eqns. (5.9) and (5.10). The approximate results obtained in this way are generally sufficiently accurate for the calculation of forced oscillations.

Let $E$ be the R.M.S. value of the applied voltage and $E_0$ the R.M.S. value of the voltage that would be obtained on open circuit with the same field voltage $e_{f0}$. Then

$$E = \frac{E_m}{\sqrt{2}},$$

$$E_0 = \frac{1}{\sqrt{2}}\left(-\frac{x_{md}}{r_f}e_{f0}\right).$$

The negative sign in the expression for $E_0$ indicates that, with the sign conventions used, a negative field voltage is required to generate a positive armature voltage.

By substituting these values in Eqns. (9.13) to (9.16), and putting $r_a = 0$, the following expressions for the steady currents and flux linkages are obtained.

$$\left.\begin{aligned} \omega\psi_{d0} &= -\sqrt{2}E\cos\delta_0 \\ \omega\psi_{q0} &= \sqrt{2}E\sin\delta_0 \\ i_{d0} &= \frac{\sqrt{2}}{x_d}(-E\cos\delta_0 + E_0) \\ i_{q0} &= \frac{\sqrt{2}}{x_q}E\sin\delta_0 \end{aligned}\right\}. \qquad \dots(9.23)$$

Substituting $\psi_{d0}$ and $\psi_{q0}$ from Eqns. (9.23) in Eqns. (9.18) and (9.19), with $r_a=0$, and rearranging, gives the following pair of simultaneous equations:

$$jm\varDelta\Psi_d+\omega\varDelta\Psi_q=\frac{\sqrt{2}E}{\omega}(jm\sin\delta_0+\omega\cos\delta_0)\varDelta\delta,$$

$$-\omega\varDelta\Psi_d+jm\varDelta\Psi_q=\frac{\sqrt{2}E}{\omega}(-\omega\sin\delta_0+jm\cos\delta_0)\varDelta\delta.$$

The solution of these equations, in conjunction with Eqns. (9.20) and (9.21), gives the oscillations of the currents and flux linkages.

$$\left.\begin{aligned}
\omega\varDelta\Psi_d&=\sqrt{2}E\sin\delta_0\varDelta\delta\\
\omega\varDelta\Psi_q&=\sqrt{2}E\cos\delta_0\varDelta\delta\\
\varDelta I_d&=\frac{\sqrt{2}E}{x_d(jm)}\sin\delta_0\varDelta\delta\\
\varDelta I_q&=\frac{\sqrt{2}E}{x_q(jm)}\cos\delta_0\varDelta\delta
\end{aligned}\right\}\quad\quad\ldots(9.24)$$

The elastic and damping constants $K$ and $C$ (see page 165) are obtained by substituting the values given by Eqns. (9.23) and (9.24) in Eqn. (9.22), and dividing by $\varDelta\delta$.

$$\frac{\varDelta F}{\varDelta\delta}=\frac{EE_0}{x_d}\cos\delta_0+E^2\cos^2\delta_0\left(\frac{1}{x_q(jm)}-\frac{1}{x_d}\right)$$
$$+E^2\sin^2\delta_0\left(\frac{1}{x_d(jm)}-\frac{1}{x_q}\right)$$
$$=K+jmC. \quad\quad\ldots(9.25)$$

The constants $K$ and $C$, determined by calculating the real and imaginary parts of Eqn. (9.25), are both functions of $m$. The manner in which they vary with the frequency is indicated in Fig. 52. It may be noted that, when $m$ is put equal to zero, the expression for $\varDelta F/\varDelta\delta$ corresponds to that for $P_0$ in Eqn. (5.10). Hence the spring constant is $P_0$ and the damping constant is zero. It is evident that the old approximate method explained on page 166 uses constants which would be correct for very low frequencies, but may be quite inaccurate for the frequencies actually occurring, particularly if the machine has a heavy damper winding.

*Calculations for a diesel-driven generator*

The values of $K$ and $mC$, calculated from Eqn. (9.25) for a 2600 kVA., 28-pole, diesel-driven alternator, are plotted in Fig. 52 as functions of frequency. A preliminary calculation

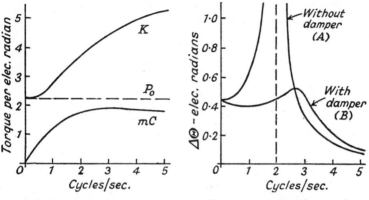

FIG. 52.—Elastic and damping constants of a synchronous machine at varying frequency.

FIG. 53.—Angular pulsation of a synchronous machine at varying frequency.

based on the old approximate method showed that the natural frequency (1·93 cycles/sec.) was very close to the frequency of the forced oscillation (1·78 cycles/sec.) produced by the four-stroke diesel engine. The alternator was provided with a heavy damper winding. Fig. 52 shows that the elastic and damping constants at the frequency of the oscillation differ greatly from those for zero frequency.

With the aid of the curves of Fig. 52 the angular pulsation produced by an applied torque pulsation may be calculated, using the formula of Eqn. (9.10). Fig. 53 gives two response curves showing the value of $\Delta\Theta$ at different frequencies for a torque pulsation equal to unity. Curve $A$, marked 'without damper', is calculated by the old approximate method using $K = P_0$, and $C = 0$. On this curve the angular pulsation becomes

171

infinite at 1·93 cycles/sec., the natural frequency. The more accurate curve $B$, marked 'with damper', is calculated from the values of $K$ and $C$ given in Fig. 52. Curve $B$ shows that the maximum angular pulsation is obtained at a frequency appreciably higher than the so-called natural frequency.

The magnitude of the torque pulsation depends on the degree of unbalance of the engine cylinders, and is difficult to estimate. It is a common assumption that the amplitude of the pulsation is equal to 10% of the rated torque. The rated power factor of the alternator is 0·8, and hence the applied torque pulsation is 0·08 per-unit at 1·78 cycles/sec. From curve $B$ of Fig. 53, the angular deviation with this applied torque at 1·78 cycles/sec. is 0·034 electrical radian, or 2·0 electrical degrees. British Standard Specification No. 649 specifies that the angular deviation should not exceed $2\frac{1}{2}$ electrical degrees.

The calculation of the angular pulsation and of the natural frequency of an undamped machine depends on the assumption that the machine is connected to a rigid supply system. When the supply is provided by several engine-driven generators operating in parallel, this condition is not satisfied. The natural frequency of an undamped machine then changes according to the particular combination of generators. For such conditions the use of a damper winding is to be recommended, because it renders the operation independent of any natural frequency. The problem is discussed in more detail in Ref. 50.2.

*Self-excitation or hunting of synchronous machines*

The results obtained by neglecting $r_a$ are accurate enough for calculating the forced oscillations due to external torque pulsations, but the method is of no value for studying self-excited oscillations, because it is readily shown from Eqn. (9.25) that, if $r_a$ is zero, the damping constant $C$ is always positive. Self-excitation depends, in fact, on the presence of appreciable armature resistance, as mentioned on page 164.

An investigation of the problem for any particular machine can be made by calculating the values of $K$ and $C$ from Eqns. (9.18) to (9.22), without neglecting $r_a$. The following result is obtained by assuming that $m$ is small compared with $\omega$, so that $\omega^2 - m^2 \approx \omega^2$.

$$\frac{\Delta \mathbf{F}}{\Delta \delta} = \frac{1}{2D}\{\omega^2(A\psi_{q0}{}^2 + B\psi_{d0}{}^2) - \omega(\psi_{d0}i_{d0} + \psi_{q0}i_{q0})$$

$$+\frac{jm}{\omega}r_a[\omega^2 AB(\psi_{d0}{}^2 + \psi_{q0}{}^2) - \omega(B-A)(\psi_{q0}i_{q0} - \psi_{d0}i_{d0})$$

$$-(i_{d0}{}^2 + i_{q0}{}^2)]$$

$$+r_a{}^2[\omega AB(\psi_{d0}i_{d0} + \psi_{q0}i_{q0}) - (Ai_{d0}{}^2 + Bi_{q0}{}^2)]\}$$

$$= K + jmC, \qquad\qquad\qquad \ldots(9.26)$$

where $A = \dfrac{1}{x_d(jm)}$,

$\qquad B = \dfrac{1}{x_q(jm)}$,

$\qquad D = 1 + \dfrac{jm}{\omega}r_a(A+B) + r_a{}^2 AB.$

For any given steady condition of operation the values of $K$ and $mC$ can be calculated at any oscillation frequency, and the criterion explained on page 167 can be used to determine whether the machine is liable to hunt. The expression in Eqn. (9.26) is, however, a very cumbersome one, and it is not easy to draw general conclusions about the conditions which determine whether hunting can occur. Simplified treatments are given in Refs. 30.3, 34.2 and 51.2.

173

# CHAPTER X

## *Approximate Methods for Generator and System Analysis*

### 39. The Problems of Power-system Analysis

The last three chapters have explained methods by which complete solutions, based on the general equations, can be obtained for several problems relating to synchronous machines. In these solutions, approximations depending on the relative order of magnitude of the constants have frequently been made in order to simplify the results, but all the assumptions made about the machine in Sects. 24 and 25 in deriving Eqns. (6.19) have been maintained.

In Chap. VIII a complete solution was given for the current following a symmetrical short circuit on a generator, assuming that the speed of the generator remained constant after the short circuit. Similar but more complicated problems arise when a short circuit or other sudden change occurs at any point in a power system, which may include several generators connected together with transformers, transmission lines, and other apparatus. For such a system a complete solution would be much too difficult, and it is necessary to make further simplifying assumptions.

The transient currents which flow after a sudden change in a power system can be divided into transient, subtransient, and asymmetrical components in the same way as the short-circuit currents considered in Chap. VIII. For many purposes it is not necessary to obtain a complete solution; for example, it may be permissible to neglect the asymmetrical component and determine only the alternating component. Simplified results of this kind are obtained if certain modifications are made to the basic assumptions, as explained later. Different assumptions are made according to which of the components are important in the particular problem.

For power-system analysis, even when a network analyser is

174

used, it is desirable for the sake of simplicity to represent each generator by a constant driving voltage with a constant series impedance. This method of representation of the generator in the equivalent circuit of the system introduces some very drastic assumptions which are explained in Sect. 40.

The practical problems of power-system analysis may be classified under four headings. The nature of the assumptions underlying the methods used for solving them are explained and discussed in the following pages. It is important to understand what assumptions have been made in applying the methods to any particular problem in order to assess whether the results are reliable.

1. *Steady operation.* A cylindrical-rotor synchronous machine can be accurately represented by a constant driving voltage and the synchronous reactance, if saturation is neglected. A salient-pole machine is frequently represented, as an approximation, in the same way using its direct-axis synchronous reactance. The principal difficulty in applying the method is to determine the appropriate values of voltage and reactance to allow for saturation (see Ref. 35.2).

2. *Fault and short-circuit conditions.* The peak current following a fault is important because it determines the rating of switchgear and the maximum forces on the conductors in machines and transformers. In order to calculate the peak value, the initial values of the components of the current must be determined, but the way in which the current dies away is not important.

3. *Transient stability.* For the study of the transient stability of a power system the transient component of any current is the important part, because the subtransient and asymmetrical components die away rapidly. Because of the slow rate of decay of the transient component it is often permissible to ignore its decrement. The determination of the *swing curve* of a generator, showing the variation of its load angle after a transient disturbance, requires a progressive calculation for which the generator is commonly assumed to have a constant reactance, the value of which is the "transient reactance" (see page 153).

4. *Variation of current or voltage after a sudden change.* It is

often necessary to determine the manner of variation of the current or voltage after a sudden change, such as the sudden application or removal of a load. Often also the action of a voltage regulator in restoring the voltage to its original value must be investigated.

## 40. Equivalent Circuits and Vector Diagrams for Approximate Calculations

The use of equivalent circuits for determining the transient performance of a generator after a sudden change depends on the assumption that the rate of change of the alternating quantities is slow in relation to the A.C. cycle; that is, that the voltages induced in either axis coil by the rate of change of the flux on that axis can be ignored. With this assumption the solution of the short-circuit problem discussed in Chap. VIII is considerably simplified. It is found that, if the above assumption is made, and if also the armature resistance is neglected, a solution of the equations gives correctly the alternating component of the current, but omits altogether the asymmetrical and second harmonic components (Ref. 51.7).

If the direct- and quadrature-axis voltages are suddenly reduced by $V_d$ and $V_q$ respectively, as assumed in Sect. 34, the armature voltage equations are Eqns. (8.16). If then $p\psi_d$ is put equal to zero in the direct-axis equation, and $p\psi_q$ is put equal to zero in the quadrature-axis equation, Eqns. (8.16) become, with $r_a=0$,

$$\left. \begin{aligned} -V_d\mathbf{1} &= \omega\psi_q \\ V_q\mathbf{1} &= \omega\psi_d \end{aligned} \right\}. \qquad \qquad ...(10.1)$$

*Equivalent circuits for the alternating components of current*

Considering first the equations for the direct-axis coils, the changes in the direct-axis currents are given by Eqns. (6.17), with $e_f=0$. These now become:

$$\left. \begin{aligned} \frac{V_q}{\omega}p\mathbf{1} &= L_{md}pi_f + L_{md}pi_{kd} + (L_{md}+l_a)pi_d \\ 0 &= \{r_f+(L_{md}+l_f)p\} + L_{md}pi_{kd} + L_{md}pi_d \\ 0 &= L_{md}pi_f + \{r_{kd}+(L_{md}+l_{kd})p\}i_{kd} + L_{md}pi_d \end{aligned} \right\}. \quad ....(10.2)$$

The applied voltage $\dfrac{V_q}{\omega} p\mathbf{1}$ in these equations is an 'impulse . voltage' of infinite magnitude and zero duration, which arises because of the sudden change of the flux $\psi_d$. The direct-axis current $i_d$ is due solely to the quadrature-axis voltage $V_q$. Similarly, as shown later, $i_q$ is due solely to $V_d$.

The solution for $i_d$ of these equations can be carried out by eliminating $i_f$ and $i_{kd}$, and using the partial fraction method in the same way as for the complete solution in Sect 32. The operational equation is:

$$i_d = \frac{1}{x_d(p)} V_q \mathbf{1},$$

$$= \frac{(1+T_{d0}'p)(1+T_{d0}''p)}{(1+T_d'p)(1+T_d''p)} \frac{V_q}{x_d} \mathbf{1}. \qquad \ldots(10.3)$$

The solution for $i_d$ as a function of time is:

$$i_d = \frac{V_q}{x_d} + \left(\frac{V_q}{x_d'} - \frac{V_q}{x_d}\right)\varepsilon^{-t/T_d'} + \left(\frac{V_q}{x_d''} - \frac{V_q}{x_d'}\right)\varepsilon^{-t/T_d''}, \quad \ldots(10.4)$$

and the corresponding component of the phase current $i_{a1}$, using the transformation Eqn. (6.2) with $\theta = (\omega t + \lambda)$, is given by:

$$i_{a1} = \left[\frac{V_q}{x_d} + \left(\frac{V_q}{x_d'} - \frac{V_q}{x_d}\right)\varepsilon^{-t/T_d'} + \left(\frac{V_q}{x_d''} - \frac{V_q}{x_d'}\right)\varepsilon^{-t/T_d''}\right] \cos(\omega t + \lambda).$$
$$\ldots(10.5)$$

Hence the solution obtained by assuming that the changes are slow gives only the alternating component of the current. For problems where the alternating component is the only one that matters, the work of obtaining the solution is very much reduced.

The equivalent circuit (Fig. 42(a)), with $e_f = 0$, and with the value of $\psi_d$ given by Eqn. (10.1), now becomes that shown in Fig. 54 (circuit $Da$). The current that flows in this circuit, when the voltage $(V_q/\omega)p\mathbf{1}$ is applied, is the unidirectional part of the direct-axis current $i_d$, and corresponds to the alternating component $i_{a1}$ of the phase current.

In a similar way the alternating current component $i_{a2}$, due to the voltage $V_d$, can be found. The equations are, from Eqns. (6.15) and (10.1):

$$\left. \begin{aligned} -\frac{V_d}{\omega}p\mathbf{1} &= L_{mq}pi_{kq} + (L_{mq}+l_a)pi_q, \\ 0 &= \{r_{kq} + (L_{mq}+l_{kq})p\}i_{kq} + L_{mq}pi_q \end{aligned} \right\} . \quad \dots(10.6)$$

The operational solution is:

$$i_q = -\frac{1}{x_q(p)}V_d\mathbf{1} = -\frac{(1+T_{q0}''p)}{(1+T_q''p)}\frac{V_d}{x_q}\mathbf{1}. \qquad \dots(10.7)$$

The solution for $i_q$ as a function of time is:

$$i_q = -\left[\frac{V_d}{x_q} + \left(\frac{V_d}{x_q''} - \frac{V_d}{x_q}\right)\varepsilon^{-t/T_q''}\right], \qquad \dots(10.8)$$

and the corresponding phase current $i_{a2}$ is given by:

$$i_{a2} = -\left[\frac{V_d}{x_q} + \left(\frac{V_d}{x_q''} - \frac{V_d}{x_q}\right)\varepsilon^{-t/T_q''}\right]\sin(\omega t + \lambda). \ \dots(10.9)$$

The quadrature-axis equivalent circuit (Fig. 42($b$)) now becomes that shown in Fig. 54 (circuit $Qa$), which is similar to the direct-axis circuit $Da$, except that there is no field winding branch.

Thus by means of the equivalent circuits $Da$ and $Qa$ of Fig. 54, the alternating component of the current which flows after the voltage is suddenly changed is obtained as the sum of three parts:

1. The original current $i_{a0}$.
2. The current $i_{a1}$, obtained from the current $i_d$, which flows in the direct-axis circuit $Da$ when $(V_q/\omega)p\mathbf{1}$ is applied.
3. The current $i_{a2}$, obtained from the current $i_q$, which flows in the quadrature-axis circuit $Qa$ when $-(V_d/\omega)p\mathbf{1}$ is applied.

The instantaneous values of the components of the applied voltage in phase $A$ are given by Eqns. (8.2). Thus each of the currents given by Eqns. (10.5) and (10.9) lags 90° behind the voltage producing it, $i_{a1}$ being produced by $[e_{a0}]_q$, and $i_{a2}$ by $[e_{a0}]_d$.

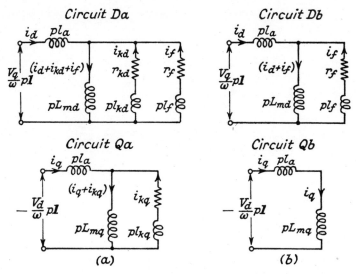

FIG. 54.—Equivalent circuits for the alternating components of the current.
(a) Including the subtransient component.
(b) Neglecting the subtransient component.

### Equivalent circuits for the alternating components of current, neglecting the subtransient part

For many purposes the subtransient components, which die away quickly, can be neglected when calculating the current following a short circuit or other sudden change of voltage. The equivalent circuits can then be simplified to circuits *Db* for the direct axis, and *Qb* for the quadrature axis. With these simplifications the direct-axis current consists only of a steady component and a transient component, while the quadrature-axis current attains the final steady value immediately.

### Equivalent circuits for the initial values of the alternating components

When the problem is such that it is only necessary to determine the initial value of the transient current, further simplifications can be made. The current dies away because of the dissipation of energy in the resistance of the field and damper windings. If these resistances were zero, the initial current would be maintained indefinitely.

Considering first the direct-axis currents, the equations simplify to the following ordinary algebraic equations (containing no operators), if the resistances of the field and damper windings are assumed to be zero.

$$\left.\begin{array}{l} V_q = x_{md}i_f + x_{md}i_{kd} + (x_{md}+x_a)i_d \\ 0 = (x_{md}+x_f)i_f + x_{md}i_{kd} + x_{md}i_d \\ 0 = x_{md}i_f + (x_{md}+x_{kd})i_{kd} + x_{md}i_d \end{array}\right\} \quad \dots(10.10)$$

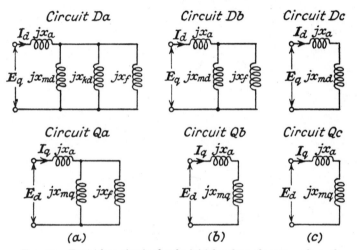

FIG. 55.—Equivalent circuits for the initial and steady-state values of the current.
(a) Including the subtransient component.
(b) Neglecting the subtransient component.
(c) Steady-state condition.

Eqns. (10.10) determine a constant value of $i_d$ equal to the initial value $V_q/x_d''$ of the expression in Eqn. (10.5). The corresponding phase current $i_{a1}$ is an alternating current, which does not die away, given by:

$$i_{a1} = \frac{V_q}{x_d''}\cos(\omega t + \lambda).$$

The equivalent circuits of Fig. 55 can be used to determine the initial transient values. The current $i_{a1}$ and the corresponding voltage $e_{a2}$ are the instantaneous values of current and voltage represented by vectors $\mathbf{I}_d$ and $\mathbf{E}_q$, such that $\mathbf{I}_d$ lags $90°$ behind $\mathbf{E}_q$. Because of the relations between the axis quantities and the components of the phase vectors during steady operation (see page 133), Eqns. (10.10) show that $\mathbf{I}_d$ is the current that flows in the simplified A.C. equivalent circuit $Da$ of Fig. 55 when the applied voltage is $\mathbf{E}_q$. The expression for $x_d''$ on page 123 shows that the overall reactance of the circuit $Da$ is the direct-axis subtransient reactance $x_d''$. Similarly the corresponding quadrature-axis circuit is $Qa$ of Fig. 55, of which the overall reactance is the quadrature-axis subtransient reactance $x_q''$.

The currents given by the circuits $Da$ and $Qa$ of Fig. 55 are the initial currents, allowing for the effect of the damper winding. If the subtransient component is neglected, as it can be for many purposes, the circuits reduce to $Db$ and $Qb$, in which the damper coils are omitted. The expression for $x_d'$ on page 123 shows that the overall reactance of circuit $Db$ is the direct-axis transient reactance $x_d'$, while that of circuit $Qb$ is the quadrature-axis synchronous reactance $x_q$, which applies for the transient condition as well as for the steady state. The current obtained with these circuits is the initial value that would be obtained if the rapidly decaying subtransient component were not present. For example, referring to Fig. 48, the short-circuit current calculated from the equivalent circuit $Db$ of Fig. 55 has a constant alternating value, for which the magnitude is given by the line $CD$, instead of the varying value given by the curve $AB$.

For the sake of completeness the steady-state equivalent circuits $Dc$ and $Qc$ are also given in Fig. 55. The overall reactances of these circuits are the synchronous reactances.

For the simplified condition to which the method applies the alternating voltages and currents are assumed to have definite values at any instant, because, apart from the sudden initial change, the rate of change of the quantities is slow compared with the A.C. cycle. The sudden initial change is a quick change of the alternating value. When the additional assumption is made that all resistances are zero, the effect of a sudden change of the A.C. voltage at the alternator terminals is simply to change the current from one A.C. value to another. The change

181

of current can be calculated from two components, one flowing in the direct-axis equivalent circuit when the quadrature-axis voltage is applied, and the other flowing in the quadrature-axis circuit when the direct-axis voltage is applied. If the resistances were really zero the current would remain at this value indefinitely, but in a practical case where the resistances are not zero, the current calculated by this method is the initial value. As time passes the current changes and finally attains the steady value.

The general definitions of the transient and subtransient reactances given in the A.I.E.E. Standard Definitions (Ref. 41.1), are based on the conception of a transient change from one A.C. value to another, as explained above. Each reactance is defined as the ratio of the component of a sudden change of voltage to the resulting change of current when only the initial value of the alternating component is considered, and the asymmetrical component is ignored. In addition to these general definitions, there are alternative A.I.E.E. definitions of the direct-axis reactances, based on the sudden short-circuit test, which is the normal method of measuring these quantities, as explained in Sect. 33.

The particular equivalent circuit to be used depends on the requirements of the problem. If the initial value of the current, including the subtransient component, is required, the circuits $Da$ and $Qa$ would be used. If, however, the subtransient component can be neglected the appropriate circuits are $Db$ and $Qb$. Circuits $Dc$ and $Qc$ apply for steady conditions.

*The constant-flux-linkage theorem*

The constant-flux-linkage theorem, due to Doherty (Ref. 23.1), has been frequently used for the study of transient phenomena in synchronous machines. The theorem depends on the well-known fact that the flux linkage with an inductive circuit having zero resistance cannot change, whatever may occur in other mutually coupled circuits. In the practical case, where resistance is present, it is still true that the flux linkage with an inductive circuit cannot change suddenly. If a sudden change, such as a short circuit, occurs in a coupled circuit, the flux linkage with the closed circuit remains unaltered for the first instant, but changes in time to a final steady value as energy is absorbed in the resistance.

In applying the constant-flux-linkage theorem to the synchronous machine, the additional assumption is usually made that the alternating quantities change slowly. Without this additional assumption, the theorem leads to a solution containing an asymmetrical component, as obtained by Doherty and Nickle in Ref. 30.2. When both assumptions are made, the constant-flux-linkage method gives the initial value of the alternating component, exactly as obtained from the A.C. equivalent circuits of Fig. 55, which were based on the assumption of zero resistance. Since the equivalent circuits show more clearly how the results are obtained, they are used here in preference to the constant-flux-linkage method.

*The two-axis vector diagram for transient changes*

The equivalent circuits $Da$ and $Qa$ of Fig. 55 give the relations between the change of voltage and the change of current in a generator after any sudden change. When the generator is connected to a power system the sudden change may be due to a fault or a switching operation at any point in the system. From the relations given by the equivalent circuits it is possible to construct a vector diagram which can be used to determine the initial voltage and current after the change.

Let $\Delta\mathbf{E}_d$ and $\Delta\mathbf{E}_q$ be the sudden changes in the components of voltage, and $\Delta\mathbf{I}_d$ and $\Delta\mathbf{I}_q$ the corresponding changes in the components of current, assuming that the three phases remain balanced throughout. Then from circuits $Da$ and $Qa$ of Fig. 55, of which the overall reactances are $x_d''$ and $x_q''$ respectively:

$$\Delta\mathbf{E}_q = jx_d''\Delta\mathbf{I}_d,$$

$$\Delta\mathbf{E}_d = jx_q''\Delta\mathbf{I}_q.$$

Hence

$$\left.\begin{array}{l}\mathbf{E}_q - jx_d''\mathbf{I}_d = \text{constant} = \mathbf{E}_q'' \ (\text{say})\\ \mathbf{E}_d - jx_q''\mathbf{I}_q = \text{constant} = \mathbf{E}_d'' \ (\text{say})\end{array}\right\} \qquad \ldots(10.11)$$

Thus for a short period after a sudden change (during which $\mathbf{E}$ and $\mathbf{I}$ change) brought about by a fault or the operation of a switch anywhere in the system, the voltages $\mathbf{E}_d''$ and $\mathbf{E}_q''$, obtained by adding the 'subtransient reactance drops' $(-jx_d''\mathbf{I}_d)$ and $(-jx_q''\mathbf{I}_q)$ to the components $\mathbf{E}_q$ and $\mathbf{E}_d$ of the terminal voltage, remain unaltered. The relations are shown on Fig. 56, which is a vector diagram similar to Fig. 37, except that the armature resistance $r_a$ is neglected. $PL''$ is the direct-axis subtransient reactance drop $(-jx_d''\mathbf{I}_d)$, and $L''N''$ is the quadrature-axis subtransient reactance drop $(-jx_q''\mathbf{I}_q)$. $ON''$ is $\mathbf{E}''$, the resultant of $\mathbf{E}_d''$ and $\mathbf{E}_q''$, and is called the 'voltage behind subtransient reactance'. The voltage $\mathbf{E}''$ remains initially unaltered after any sudden change.

If the machine has no damper winding, or if the conditions of the problem are such that the rapidly decaying subtransient components of voltage and current can be neglected, the relations between the sudden changes of voltage and current are given by the equivalent circuits $Db$ and $Qb$ of Fig. 55, of which the overall reactances are $x_d'$ and $x_q$ respectively:

$$\varDelta\mathbf{E}_q = jx_d'\varDelta\mathbf{I}_d,$$

$$\varDelta\mathbf{E}_d = jx_q\varDelta\mathbf{I}_q.$$

Hence

$$\left.\begin{array}{l}\mathbf{E}_q - jx_d'\mathbf{I}_d = \text{constant} = \mathbf{E}_q' \text{ (say)} \\ \mathbf{E}_d - jx_q\mathbf{I}_q = \text{constant} = \mathbf{E}_d' \text{ (say)}\end{array}\right\} \quad \ldots(10.12)$$

Thus for the effective initial condition ignoring the subtransient components, the voltages $\mathbf{E}_q'$ and $\mathbf{E}_d'$, obtained by adding the 'transient reactance drops' $(-jx_d'\mathbf{I}_d)$ and $(-jx_q\mathbf{I}_q)$ to the components $\mathbf{E}_q$ and $\mathbf{E}_d$ of the terminal voltage, remain unaltered. In Fig. 56, $PL'$ is the direct-axis transient reactance drop $(-jx_d'\mathbf{I}_d)$ and $L'N'$ is the quadrature-axis synchronous reactance drop $(-jx_q\mathbf{I}_q)$. $ON'$ is $\mathbf{E}'$, the resultant of $\mathbf{E}_d'$ and $\mathbf{E}_q'$, and is called the 'voltage behind transient reactance'. The voltage $\mathbf{E}'$ remains initially unaltered after any sudden change.

Fig. 56 also shows the steady-state vector diagram, in which the synchronous reactance drops $(-jx_d\mathbf{I}_d)$ and $(-jx_q\mathbf{I}_q)$ are added to the terminal voltage. $ON$ is $\mathbf{E}_0$, the 'voltage behind synchronous reactance', which remains unaltered for any condition of steady operation.

The vector diagrams for the two alternative types of transient condition are similar to the steady-state diagram, differing only in the values of reactance used. Hence the use of the vector diagram to determine the initial currents after a sudden change follows the same lines as the steady-state two-axis method.

*Simplified vector diagrams for transient changes*

When the generator is connected to a power system the calculations required by the two-axis theory become rather

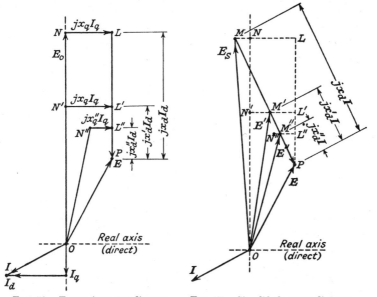

FIG. 56.—Two-axis vector diagram for the initial current and voltage.

FIG. 57.—Simplified vector diagram for the initial current and voltage.

complicated. The method is greatly simplified if the assumption is made that each quadrature-axis reactance is equal to the corresponding direct-axis reactance, that is:

$$x_q = x_d \quad \text{(cylindrical-rotor machine)},$$

$$x_q = x_d' \quad \text{(zero 'transient saliency')},$$

$$x_q'' = x_d'' \quad \text{(zero 'subtransient saliency')}.$$

Fig. 57 is a vector diagram showing the result of these assumptions. The points $N$, $N'$ and $N''$ on the two-axis diagram (shown dotted) move to $M$, $M'$ and $M''$, which all

185

lie on a straight line through $P$ perpendicular to the current vector $\mathbf{I}$. $PM$ is the synchronous reactance drop $(-jx_d\mathbf{I})$, $PM'$ is the transient reactance drop $(-jx_d'\mathbf{I})$, and $PM''$ is the subtransient reactance drop $(-jx_d''\mathbf{I})$.

The assumption that $x_q=x_d$ for steady operation means that the generator is treated as a cylindrical-rotor machine. $\mathbf{E}_s$, the voltage behind synchronous reactance, is then equal to $OM$, and the generator can be represented by a source of constant voltage $\mathbf{E}_s$ with the synchronous reactance $x_d$ in series. $\mathbf{E}_s$ differs from $\mathbf{E}_0$ because of the changed value of $x_q$.

For calculations relating to 'slow' transient changes, for which the subtransient components can be neglected, the assumption is that $x_q=x_d'$. The machine is said to have 'zero transient saliency', a condition which is quite different from that of having a cylindrical rotor because of the effect of the field winding. The assumption is in fact more nearly true of a salient-pole generator than of a turbo-alternator. With this assumption, $\mathbf{E}'$, the voltage behind transient reactance, is equal to $OM'$, and the generator can be represented by a source of constant voltage $\mathbf{E}'$ with the transient reactance $x_d'$ in series.

For the calculation of 'rapid' transients, where the initial values of voltage and current immediately after a sudden change are required, the approximate method assumes that the machine has 'zero subtransient saliency', or that $x_q''=x_d''$. For most modern machines the assumption is a reasonable one, particularly as the subtransient reactance is small compared with the reactances in the external power system. $\mathbf{E}''$, the voltage behind subtransient reactance, is equal to $OM''$ in Fig. 56, and the generator can be represented by a source of constant voltage $\mathbf{E}''$ with the subtransient reactance $x_d''$ in series.

### 41. The Analysis of Unbalanced Conditions

When the circuits to which a generator is connected are not balanced between the three phases the conditions are much more complicated than when the circuits are balanced. It has already been shown in Sect. 31 that during steady operation negative-sequence applied voltages give rise not only to negative-sequence currents but also to third harmonic currents. Similarly negative-sequence currents give rise to third harmonic voltages. In the general case, when the voltages and currents are not specified, but are related to each other in a manner determined by the external circuits, both voltage and current must be expressed by an infinite series of harmonics. Under transient conditions the voltage and current can be split up into components which decay at different rates, but each component contains an infinite series of harmonics.

With the assumption that the speed remains unchanged at the synchronous speed $\omega$, Eqns. (6.7) give:

$$\left.\begin{aligned} e_d &= p\psi_d + \omega\psi_q + r_a i_d \\ e_q &= -\omega\psi_d + p\psi_q + r_a i_q \end{aligned}\right\}. \qquad \ldots(10.13)$$

The equations for the axis quantities are thus of a linear form, but the values of $e_d$ and $e_q$ are not known explicitly, as they are for a symmetrical short circuit. There are additional relations between the axis voltages and currents depending on the external connections, but they are in such a form that the ordinary operational methods cannot be used. Complete solutions for the principal unbalanced short-circuit conditions have, however, been obtained. For more general conditions, when the generator is connected to an external system, it is only feasible to use approximate methods similar to those explained in the last section. For unbalanced conditions the method of symmetrical components is used and involves the assumption that all harmonics can be neglected.

The analysis of a single-phase short circuit on a synchronous generator was first given by Doherty and Nickle (Ref. 28.1), who derived expressions for the transient currents in the armature and field circuits and verified them by means of oscillographic tests. A very full theoretical treatment of the three alternative types of short circuit of a three-phase generator (line to line, line to neutral, and double line to neutral) is given by Concordia (Ref. 51.1). For each case expressions are given for the transient torque and the open phase voltages as well as for the currents. The method used by these authors is to derive the initial values of the components of the currents by approximate methods and to estimate a time constant appropriate to each component.

A more rigorous and complete analysis of unbalanced conditions on synchronous machines is given in Ref. 54.2, which uses the Laplace transform method. This work provides a means of calculating the harmonics during steady unbalanced operation and gives a general formulation of the transient problem. The solutions obtained for the short-circuit conditions confirm the results of Refs. 28.1 and 51.1.

In order to indicate the nature of the problem, the particular case of a line-to-line short circuit is considered in the next few pages. The discussion merely gives a statement of the equations and of the expression obtained for the armature current. For a more detailed treatment the references quoted above should be consulted.

### Line-to-line short circuit

The phase voltages and currents obey the following relations if phases $B$ and $C$ are short-circuited when the generator is running on open circuit.

$$i_a = 0,$$
$$i_b = -i_c,$$
$$e_b = e_c.$$

Using the transformation equations (6.2) and (6.4), the following relations between the axis quantities are obtained:

$$\left. \begin{array}{l} i_d \cos \theta + i_q \sin \theta = 0 \\ e_d \sin \theta - e_q \cos \theta = 0 \end{array} \right\}, \qquad \dots(10.14)$$

where $\theta = \omega t + \lambda$.

Eqns. (10.14) together with (10.13), (6.9), (6.12), and the known initial conditions determine the voltages and currents. The solution is, however, difficult because the coefficients now include functions of time, and the principal advantage obtained by transforming to axis quantities is thereby lost. The solutions given in the references do not in fact use the axis quantities, but either determine the three-phase currents and voltages directly or introduce equivalent two-phase quantities ($\alpha - \beta$ components). Whatever method is used for formulating the equations, the solution is much more difficult than for the symmetrical condition.

188

The expression for the short-circuit current obtained by solving the equations is:

$$i_b = \sqrt{3}E\left[\frac{1}{x_d+x_2} + \left(\frac{1}{x_d'+x_2} - \frac{1}{x_d+x_2}\right)\varepsilon^{-t/T_{d'(1-1)}}\right.$$

$$\left. + \left(\frac{1}{x_d''+x_2} - \frac{1}{x_d'+x_2}\right)\varepsilon^{-t/T_{d''(1-1)}} \right]\sum_{n=0}^{\infty}(-b)^n\cos(2n-1)\theta$$

$$+ \frac{\sqrt{3}E\sin\lambda}{x_2}\varepsilon^{-t/T_{a(1-1)}}\left[\frac{1}{2} + \sum_{n=1}^{\infty}(-b)^n\cos 2n\theta\right], \qquad \dots(10.15)$$

where

$$\left.\begin{aligned}x_2 &= \sqrt{x_d''x_q''}\\b &= \frac{\sqrt{x_q''}-\sqrt{x_d''}}{\sqrt{x_q''}+\sqrt{x_d''}}\\T_{d'(1-1)} &= \frac{x_d'+x_2}{x_d+x_2}T_{do}'\\T_{d''(1-1)} &= \frac{x_d''+x_2}{x_d'+x_2}T_{do}''\\T_{a(1-1)} &= \frac{x_2}{\omega r_a}\end{aligned}\right\} \qquad \dots(10.16)$$

The quantities not defined here are given on pages 122 and 123.

The steady current after all transient components have died away is given by the following harmonic series:

$$[i_b]_{(steady)} = \sqrt{3}E\left(\frac{1}{x_d+x_2}\right)\sum_{n=0}^{\infty}(-b)^n\cos(2n-1)\theta.$$

$$\dots(10.17)$$

The form of the expression in Eqn. (10.15) for the current after an unbalanced short circuit is similar to the corresponding expression in Eqn. (8.11) under balanced conditions, except that the first part contains an infinite series of odd harmonics and the second part contains an infinite series of even harmonics. The magnitudes of the harmonics depend on the quantity $b$, which is zero if the two subtransient reactances $x_d''$ and $x_q''$ are equal. For an approximate analysis it is permissible to neglect the harmonics as well as the asymmetrical component included in the second part of Eqn. (10.15). The fundamental alternating component is:

$$[i_b]_{(alt)} = \sqrt{3}E\left[\frac{1}{x_d+x_2} + \left(\frac{1}{x_d'+x_2} - \frac{1}{x_d+x_2}\right)\varepsilon^{-t/T_d'(1-t)}\right.$$
$$\left. + \left(\frac{1}{x_d''+x_2} - \frac{1}{x_d'+x_2}\right)\varepsilon^{-t/T_d''(1-t)}\right]\cos(\omega t+\lambda).$$
$$...(10.18)$$

*Steady, transient and subtransient components of current*

The current given by Eqn. (10.18) is of the same form as the alternating component, given by the first part of Eqn. (8.11) for the current after a symmetrical short circuit. It consists of a steady component, a transient component and a subtransient component, but the values of the various reactances differ from those in the expression for the symmetrical short-circuit current.

The fundamental of the steady current in phase $B$ during a sustained line-to-line short circuit between phases $B$ and $C$ after all the transient components have died away is:

$$[i_b]_{st} = \frac{\sqrt{3}E}{x_d+x_2}\cos(\omega t+\lambda). \qquad ...(10.19)$$

It can readily be seen that this result agrees with that given by the theory of symmetrical components, if the positive-sequence reactance is $x_d$, and the negative-sequence reactance is $x_2$.

The initial value of the current given by Eqn. (10.18), with the subtransient component included, is:

$$[i_b]'' = \frac{\sqrt{3}E}{x_d''+x_2}\cos(\omega t+\lambda). \qquad ...(10.20)$$

The initial value, if the subtransient component is neglected, is:

$$[i_b]' = \frac{\sqrt{3}E}{x_d'+x_2}\cos(\omega t+\lambda). \qquad ...(10.21)$$

These currents agree with those given by the symmetrical component method, if the positive-sequence reactances are taken to be $x_d''$ and $x_d'$ respectively and the negative-sequence reactance to be $x_2$.

It thus appears that, for a line-to-line short circuit, the steady and the initial transient values of the fundamental alternating component of the current can be calculated in a simple manner by the method of symmetrical components. The appropriate positive-sequence reactances are the same as those for the symmetrical short circuit, and the negative-sequence reactance $x_2$ is that given in Eqns. (10.16).

The time constants $T_d'{}_{(l-l)}$ and $T_d''{}_{(l-l)}$ of the transient and subtransient components differ from the corresponding quantities $T_d'$ and $T_d''$ for the symmetrical short-circuit current. These latter time constants are given by the following expressions which are readily deduced from the formulae on page 123:

$$
\left.
\begin{aligned}
T_d' &= \frac{x_d'}{x_d} T_{d0}' \\[2mm]
T_d'' &= \frac{x_d''}{x_d'} T_{d0}''
\end{aligned}
\right\} . \qquad \ldots(10.22)
$$

The time constants for the unbalanced short circuit differ from these because of the introduction of the negative-sequence reactance $x_2$ into the formulae of Eqn. (10.16).

### General treatment of unbalanced fault conditions

If a similar analysis is made for the line-to-neutral and double-line-to-neutral short-circuit conditions, it is found that the fundamental currents can also be determined by the symmetrical component method. The appropriate positive-sequence reactances are $x_d$, $x_d'$, $x_d''$, as before, but the required values of negative-sequence reactance are different from that for the line-to-line short circuit. The zero-sequence reactance $x_0$ must also be used.

For more complicated unbalanced fault conditions of the kind encountered in power systems where several alternators are connected through transformers and transmission lines, it is thus a reasonable assumption that the fundamental fault currents can be calculated by the method of symmetrical components. The principal doubt arises in the choice of the appropriate negative-sequence reactance $x_2$. From an analysis of five different conditions, given in Ref. 49.2, Duesterhoeft has concluded that $x_2$ always lies between the two extreme values given by Eqns. (7.16) and (7.18).

$$\left.\begin{aligned}[x_2]_{\text{max.}} &= \tfrac{1}{2}(x_d'' + x_q'') \\ [x_2]_{\text{min.}} &= \frac{2x_d'' x_q''}{x_d'' + x_q''}\end{aligned}\right\} . \qquad \ldots(10.23)$$

Compared with the symmetrical condition, for which the usual approximate methods of analysis are discussed in Sect. 40, the principal additional source of error is due to the presence of harmonic components. The magnitudes of the harmonics depend on the quantity $b$, which in turn depends on the ratio of the direct and quadrature-axis subtransient reactances. For the line-to-line short circuit $b$ has the value in Eqn. (10.16), and for other conditions the expression for $b$ is different, but is of a similar type. When the two subtransient reactances $x_d''$ and $x_q''$ are equal, $b$ is zero, and there are no harmonics. It may furthermore be noted that, if $x_d'' = x_q''$, the two extreme values of $x_2$ in Eqns. (10.23) are the same.

If an alternator is liable to operate with unbalanced currents, it is very desirable, in order to reduce the harmonics, that the two subtransient reactances shall be as nearly equal as possible. The results obtained by the method of symmetrical components are then sufficiently accurate for most practical purposes of power-system analysis. When $x_d''$ and $x_q''$ are nearly equal, it is usually satisfactory to take the negative-sequence reactance $x_2$ to be equal to their arithmetic mean, as in the first expression of Eqns. (10.23). If $x_d''$ and $x_q''$ differ considerably, the calculations become inaccurate, and there are liable to be other incidental troubles; for example, excessive voltage peaks may appear on an open phase.

### 42. Application of the Approximate Methods to Power-system Analysis

The approximate methods discussed in this chapter provide the basis for simple means of determining the currents in a power system under certain conditions, since the generator can be replaced by its driving voltage and its three sequence reactances, appropriate values being selected for the particular condition. The system then becomes an ordinary network of lumped elements, and any of the well-known methods of network analysis can be used. For simple two- or three-machine systems numerical calculations may be made, but for extensive systems a network analyser or a computer becomes indispensable (see Refs. 52.2, 45.1 and 47.1).

The methods of solution for the different types of problems are discussed briefly here under the same headings as in Sect. 39.

1. *Steady operation.* The calculation of the currents flowing in a system under steady conditions when the applied voltages are known is called a *load study*. It is possible to make such a calculation by assuming that each generator has a known excitation and including its synchronous reactance in the network. The constant field corresponds to a constant 'voltage behind synchronous reactance', which is taken to be the driving voltage $E_0$. The value of reactance is, however, uncertain because of saturation, and, moreover, it is a commoner practical condition to operate the generator with a constant voltage maintained by a voltage regulator, rather than with constant excitation. Under these conditions the load study is purely a network problem, for which the generator voltage is assumed, and the generator characteristics do not enter into the calculations.

The generator characteristics are more important in the study of steady-state stability. A power system is stable in the steady state if the change in electrical torque in any generator due to a small slow change in angular position is such as to restore the generator to its original position. The stability can be checked by setting up the network analyser for the given steady condition, measuring the currents after making a small change and calculating the change of torque. The generator must be represented by its reactance and a constant driving voltage behind the reactance. If there were no saturation, the synchronous reactance would be the appropriate one, but in practice a lower value, depending on the slope of the saturation curve at the point where the small change occurs, must be used. The correct value for a steady-state stability study is known as the *effective synchronous reactance* or *equivalent reactance*, and is usually about 0·6 to 0·8 of the synchronous reactance.

2. *Fault and short-circuit conditions.* After the occurrence of a fault or a short circuit on a power system, the current immediately rises to a high value, but dies down to a new steady value in a few seconds, as shown in Fig. 47. The transient current consists of an alternating component which does not depend on the instant of switching, and an asymmetrical component which displaces the wave for a short time after the fault. The initial value of the alternating component can be determined by means of a network analyser if each generator is represented by its subtransient reactance and a constant 'voltage behind subtransient reactance', which is taken to be the driving voltage. The voltage behind subtransient reactance is the voltage $\mathbf{E}''$ introduced on page 184. The analyser is first set up for the original steady condition in order to determine the value of $\mathbf{E}''$ for each generator. The network is then modified to represent the condition after the fault, and the same value of $\mathbf{E}''$ is maintained. The current that flows at any point in the system under this condition is the initial value of the alternating component.

The maximum peak current is greater than the peak of the alternating component because of the displacement due to the asymmetrical component, and, in the worst condition with the most unfavourable instant of switching, the value may be doubled. Because of the rapid decay of the wave, the theoretical initial value is never attained, as can be seen in Fig. 47 (phase $C$), and it is usually assumed, as specified in British Standard Specification No. 116, that the maximum peak is 1·8 times the peak value of the alternating current calculated in the manner described. Thus if $I''$ is the R.M.S. current determined from the network analysis, the maximum peak current is $1·8\sqrt{2}I''$.

3. *Transient stability.* After a fault occurs on a system, the asymmetrical and subtransient components of the current die away in a small fraction of a second, but the transient effect of the disturbance continues for several seconds. If the system is stable under this transient condition, the generators ultimately settle down to a new condition of steady operation at synchronous speed. On the other hand, a severe disturbance

may lead to instability so that the generators pull out of step and have to be disconnected. The phenomenon depends greatly on the mechanical characteristics of the generators, since the rotors accelerate and decelerate, causing the instantaneous load angles to oscillate. The *transient stability* of a system is studied by calculating a *swing curve* for each generator. The swing curve gives the manner of variation of the angle $\delta$ with time (see page 159).

If the asymmetrical and subtransient components are ignored a generator may, for a short period after the fault (up to half a second), be represented by its transient reactance and a constant 'voltage behind transient reactance' $\mathbf{E}'$, as explained on page 184. The normal method of analysis of transient stability is based on this manner of representation. The method assumes that the flux linkage with the field winding remains constant during the period considered, and it introduces an error which becomes greater as time passes. The accuracy obtained is reasonable during the first swing, but the method is not reliable for determining the subsequent oscillations. In applying the method only the first swing is calculated, and it is assumed that if the generator does not pull out of step during the first swing it will ultimately settle down to a steady condition.

The calculation is carried out by a step-by-step method in which a separate determination of the generator torques is made for each of several successive small time intervals. The variation of speed during the swing is very small and the torque is taken to be proportional to the power at each instant. The torque exerted on each generator by its prime mover is assumed to remain constant during the disturbance, so that the generator rotor accelerates when the torque developed is reduced as a result of the fault. The initial change of torque is determined by calculating the currents in a manner similar to that explained on page 194, except that the transient reactance is used instead of the subtransient reactance. Each generator is represented on the analyser by a voltage $\mathbf{E}'$ and a reactance $x_d{}'$. When the accelerating torque is known the change in the angle $\delta$ during the specified time interval can be found, and each generator is then reset on the analyser with the new angle, so that new values of torque can be found for the next interval.

The step-by-step method is laborious and various types of auxiliary analysing equipment have been devised for reducing the amount of numerical computation. Moreover the accuracy is not great, because the decay of the field flux linkage and the effect of the damper winding are neglected, and because of the assumption that the direct-axis and quadrature-axis transient reactances are equal. Nevertheless, as a practical method it has proved to be of great value in studying the transient stability of power systems. The subject is discussed very fully in Ref. 47.1.

4. *Variation of current or voltage after a sudden change.* The methods so far described provide means of determining the initial values of voltage and current in a system immediately after a sudden change, as well as the final values after a steady condition has been reached. It is often necessary to know approximately how the quantities vary during the intervening period. The step-by-step method for the study of transient stability allows for the effect of the changing angle of the rotor but not for the changing flux, and provides a means of calculating how all the quantities vary under these assumptions. For other problems the swinging of the rotor is less important, but the modification of the flux distribution as time passes must be taken into account. For such problems a somewhat different method can be used, as explained below for two simple examples. The calculation is a good deal simpler than the step-by-step process but the method is a very approximate one and must be used with discretion.

By analogy with the short-circuit condition it is assumed that the change of current between the initial and final values can be divided into component currents, each of which decays exponentially with a definite time constant. The problem is therefore to determine the magnitudes and time constants for each of these components. Usually only one or two components are considered, so that there may be considerable error in applying the method to a complicated system.

*Sudden application of load to a generator*

If a load is suddenly applied to a generator running on open circuit with a constant excitation, the voltage falls and

196

eventually reaches a new steady value. The starting of a large induction motor, suddenly switched on to the generator, is a common example of this condition. There is first a rapid change and then a more gradual one, as indicated by the full line on Fig. 58. If the load is a pure reactance, the solution can be

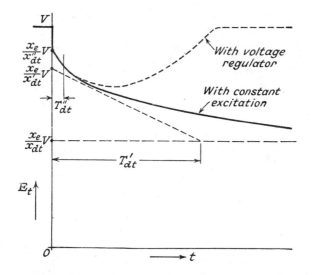

FIG. 58.—Variation of the voltage after sudden application of a load.

obtained by adding the external reactance $x_e$ to that of the generator and using the result already worked out in Sect. 32 for the short circuit. The alternating component of the current that flows after the switch is closed is, from Eqn. (10.5):

$$i_{at} = \sqrt{2}\left[\frac{V}{x_{dt}} + \left(\frac{V}{x_{dt}'} - \frac{V}{x_{dt}}\right)\varepsilon^{-t/T_{dt}'}\right.$$

$$\left. + \left(\frac{V}{x_{dt}''} - \frac{V}{x_{dt}''}\right)\varepsilon^{-t/T_{dt}''}\right]\cos\,(\omega t + \lambda), \quad ...(10.24)$$

where $V$ is the R.M.S. voltage before the load is connected, and the additional suffix $t$ indicates that $(x_a + x_e)$ must be used

197

instead of $x_a$ when the formulae of page 123 are used to calculate the constants. Thus

$$\left.\begin{aligned}
x_{dt} &= x_d + x_e \\
x_{dt}' &= x_d' + x_e \\
x_{dt}'' &= x_d'' + x_e \\
T_{dt}' &= \frac{1}{\omega r_f}\left(x_f + \frac{x_{md}(x_a+x_e)}{x_{md}+(x_a+x_e)}\right) \\
T_{dt}'' &= \frac{1}{\omega r_{kd}}\left(x_{kd} + \frac{x_{md}(x_a+x_e)x_f}{x_{md}(x_a+x_e)+x_{md}x_f+(x_a+x_e)x_f}\right)
\end{aligned}\right\} \quad \ldots (10.25)$$

The R.M.S. voltage at the alternator terminals is given by:

$$E_t = \left[\frac{x_e}{x_{dt}}V + \left(\frac{x_e}{x_{dt}'}V - \frac{x_e}{x_{dt}}V\right)\varepsilon^{-t/T_{dt}'} + \left(\frac{x_e}{x_{dt}''}V - \frac{x_e}{x_{dt}'}V\right)\varepsilon^{-t/T_{dt}''}\right].$$

$$\ldots(10.26)$$

Fig. 58 (full line) shows the variation of the terminal voltage with time. There is a sudden drop from the original voltage $V$ to the initial voltage $\dfrac{x_e}{x_d''+x_e}V$ after the change. This initial voltage could be calculated alternatively by considering the generator to have a voltage $V$ behind its subtransient reactance.

If the rapidly decaying subtransient component, given by the third term of Eqn. (10.26), is neglected the voltage drops suddenly from the original voltage $V$ to the initial voltage $\dfrac{x_e}{x_d'+x_e}V$, which would be calculated by considering the generator to have a voltage $V$ behind its transient reactance.

Finally the steady voltage $\dfrac{x_e}{x_d+x_e}V$ could be calculated in accordance with ordinary steady-state theory by considering the generator to have a voltage $V$ behind its synchronous reactance.

Thus the curve showing the variation of the terminal voltage could be calculated by using the vector diagram of Fig. 56 or Fig. 57 to determine the initial transient values and the steady value, and then fitting in appropriate time constants for the components of the change.

The transient time constant $T_{dt}'$, the value of which is given in Eqns. (10.25), depends on the external reactance. It is equal to $T_d'$ when $x_e=0$ (short circuit), and is equal to $T'_{d0}$ when $x_e=\infty$ (open circuit). For any given load impedance, $T_{dt}'$ is intermediate between these two extremes. Similarly the subtransient time constant $T_{dt}''$ is intermediate between $T_d''$ and $T_{d0}''$.

A calculation of this kind is valuable in studying the action of a voltage regulator used to maintain a constant voltage. The regulator cannot act quickly enough to prevent the rapid drop to the initial transient voltage $\dfrac{x_e}{x_d'+x_e}\,V$, but it can restore the voltage to the original value $V$ in a short time by automatically increasing the excitation, as indicated by the dotted line on Fig. 58. Such a curve can be calculated by treating the action of the voltage regulator independently and using the principle of superposition. The problem is discussed in Ref. 44.4.

*Rise of voltage after removal of load*

If the load is suddenly disconnected from an alternator the voltage rises, at first rapidly and then more slowly, until a new steady value is reached. The curve of variation of the voltage can be calculated by the method just described. Generally the subtransient effect is too rapid to be of any importance, and it is neglected in the following calculation.

If the vector diagram for the original load condition is that shown in Fig. 56, the voltage behind synchronous reactance is $E_0$. Hence if saturation is neglected, the steady voltage after the load is removed is $E_0$. The voltage behind transient reactance is $E'$, and gives the initial value of the voltage immediately after the load is removed. The appropriate time constant is the open-circuit direct-axis transient time constant $T'_{d0}$. Hence the R.M.S. voltage is given by:

$$E_t=E'+(E_0-E')(1-\varepsilon^{-t/T'_{d0}}) \qquad \ldots(10.27)$$

and is plotted in the full-line curve on Fig. 59.

The practical problem is usually to find how rapidly a voltage regulator can restore the voltage to its normal value, and what maximum value is attained. The action of the regulator, as well as the effect of changing speed of the generator after disconnection from the system, can be studied by using the principle of superposition. The dotted line in Fig. 59 shows how the

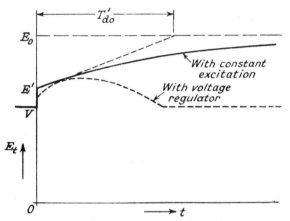

Fig. 59.—Variation of the voltage after sudden removal of a load.

voltage varies if a regulator is used. The dotted line also indicates how the curve is modified in the initial stage by the subtransient effect. It may be noted that, although the value of the steady voltage $E_0$ determined by this method would be much too high because of saturation, the calculation of the voltage curve, when a regulator is used to limit its rise, would be reasonably accurate.

# CHAPTER XI

## *The Generalised Rotating Machine*

### 43. Matrix Transformations

It has been shown that, if appropriate transformations of the variables are made where necessary, the equations of all the types of rotating machine so far considered can be expressed in the same form. In the generalised equations, the voltages and currents are associated with the two fixed axes, whether they are the actual values or new fictitious values obtained by means of a transformation. For a D.C. machine with its brushes located on one or both axes the actual values appear in the equations. In a synchronous machine the voltages and currents of the field windings are the actual values but those of the armature winding are fictitious transformed values. In an induction motor the quantities in the rotating winding must be transformed in the same way as in the synchronous machine. The stator quantities in the induction motor equations may be the actual values if the winding is two-phase, but for a three-phase winding they must be transformed to those of an equivalent two-phase winding. The transformation used to replace the actual voltages and currents in rotating windings by the fictitious axis values is essentially an algebraic substitution using a set of transformation equations.

The fact that generalised equations of a similar kind apply to all types of machine makes possible a new approach to the theory of electrical machines. Whatever the machine, the generalised equations can be written down from a diagram, like those in Figs. 5, 39 or 40, having the appropriate number of coils on the two axes required for the particular arrangement. If the generalised equations contain fictitious variables it is possible at any stage in their manipulation to transform them, by means of the appropriate substitution, into new equations containing the actual variables. More often, however, the transformation is not made until after the solution has been

201

obtained. In all the A.C. machine problems so far considered the axis equations have been solved directly, and the actual voltages and currents have been derived from the axis values by means of the transformation equations.

The matrix formed by the coefficients in a set of transformation equations is called a *transformation matrix*. In general, two sets of equations are required, one for voltages and one for currents, although the two sets are usually related to each other. The equations that transform the phase voltages and currents in a rotating three-phase winding into the axis values are given in matrix form in Eqns. (6.1) and (6.3). In this particular case the transformation matrices for voltage and current are identical. The inverse matrices in Eqns. (6.2) and (6.4), which transform axis values into phase values are also identical. The equations that transform the three-phase quantities of a stationary winding into those of an equivalent two-phase winding are given in Eqns. (6.28) and (6.30).

In addition to the phase-to-axis transformations, there are many other kinds of transformation by means of which one set of variables can be related to another set. In this chapter three other transformations are considered:

1. Transformation to reduce the number of variables when there are external connections between the circuits.
2. Transformation for a commutator winding for which the brushes are not on the axes.
3. Transformation to reduce the number of variables for balanced polyphase operation.

As already mentioned, it is possible, instead of solving the generalised equations directly, to transform them into new equations containing other variables, and to solve the transformed equations. For the synchronous machine problems this process would usually lead to more complicated equations and a more difficult solution. For other types of problem, however, the method can simplify the solution, particularly if the transformation has the effect of reducing the number of variables.

The generalised theory can thus be applied to a practical problem by the following process:

1. Draw the diagram of the generalised or 'primitive' machine.
2. Write down the generalised equations.
3. Derive a transformation matrix and transform the generalised equations so as to obtain new equations which are fewer in number or are more easily solved. The voltages and currents in the new equations are usually the actual values, but other sets of fictitious quantities may be introduced if there is advantage in so doing.

The algebraic manipulations necessary to transform the equations are best carried out by using the methods of matrix algebra. Some of the simpler methods are explained in the following pages and are applied to the solution of a number of typical problems.

*Matrix multiplication*

In matrix notation a matrix, which is an array of many distinct numbers, is represented by a single symbol enclosed in square brackets. Thus a set of equations like

$$\left.\begin{aligned} e_1 &= Z_{11}i_1 + Z_{12}i_2 + Z_{13}i_3 \\ e_2 &= Z_{21}i_1 + Z_{22}i_2 + Z_{23}i_3 \\ e_3 &= Z_{31}i_1 + Z_{32}i_2 + Z_{33}i_3 \end{aligned}\right\}, \qquad \ldots(11.1)$$

is written as a matrix equation as

$$\begin{bmatrix} e_1 \\ e_2 \\ e_3 \end{bmatrix} = \begin{bmatrix} Z_{11} & Z_{12} & Z_{13} \\ Z_{21} & Z_{22} & Z_{23} \\ Z_{31} & Z_{32} & Z_{33} \end{bmatrix} \cdot \begin{bmatrix} i_1 \\ i_2 \\ i_3 \end{bmatrix} \qquad \ldots(11.2)$$

and is abbreviated to

$$[e] = [Z].[i], \qquad \ldots(11.3)$$

where $[e]$ and $[i]$ are matrices of rank 1, and $[Z]$ is a matrix of rank 2.

The most important operation in the manipulation of matrices is that known as *matrix multiplication*. Thus in Eqn. (11.3) $[Z]$ is said to be 'multiplied' by $[i]$. Matrix multiplication is, however, a more complicated process than the multiplication of ordinary numbers, and the rules that have to be observed are different in certain respects. The principal use of matrix multiplication is to enable the algebraic substitution process required in the transformation of variables to be carried out in an organised manner, and it is best explained in this connection.

As a simple example, suppose that it is required to transform the variables $i_1$, $i_2$, $i_3$ into new variables $i_1'$, $i_2'$, related to the old variables by the following equations:

$$\left.\begin{array}{l} i_1 = C_{11}i_1' + C_{12}i_2' \\ i_2 = C_{21}i_1' + C_{22}i_2' \\ i_3 = C_{31}i_1' + C_{32}i_2' \end{array}\right\} . \qquad \ldots(11.4)$$

The matrix equation is:

$$
\begin{array}{|c|}
\hline
i_1 \\
\hline
i_2 \\
\hline
i_3 \\
\hline
\end{array}
=
\begin{array}{|c c|}
\hline
C_{11} & C_{12} \\
\hline
C_{21} & C_{22} \\
\hline
C_{31} & C_{32} \\
\hline
\end{array}
\cdot
\begin{array}{|c|}
\hline
i_1' \\
\hline
i_2' \\
\hline
\end{array}
\qquad \ldots(11.5)
$$

or

$$[i] = [C] \cdot [i']. \qquad \ldots(11.6)$$

If Eqns. (11.4) are substituted in Eqns. (11.1) the relation between $e_1$, $e_2$, $e_3$ and $i_1'$, $i_2'$, expressed as a matrix equation, is:

$$
\begin{array}{|c|}
\hline
e_1 \\
\hline
e_2 \\
\hline
e_3 \\
\hline
\end{array}
=
\begin{array}{|c c|}
\hline
Z_{11}C_{11}+Z_{12}C_{21}+Z_{13}C_{31} & Z_{11}C_{12}+Z_{12}C_{22}+Z_{13}C_{32} \\
\hline
Z_{21}C_{11}+Z_{22}C_{21}+Z_{23}C_{31} & Z_{21}C_{12}+Z_{22}C_{22}+Z_{23}C_{32} \\
\hline
Z_{31}C_{11}+Z_{32}C_{21}+Z_{33}C_{31} & Z_{31}C_{12}+Z_{32}C_{22}+Z_{33}C_{32} \\
\hline
\end{array}
\cdot
\begin{array}{|c|}
\hline
i_1' \\
\hline
i_2' \\
\hline
\end{array}
$$

$$\ldots(11.7)$$

or

$$[e] = [K] \cdot [i']. \qquad \ldots(11.8)$$

The matrix $[K]$ is said to be the *matrix product* of $[Z]$ and $[C]$.

$$[K] = [Z] \cdot [C]. \qquad \ldots(11.9)$$

The rule of matrix multiplication is thus that each element of the matrix product $[K]$ is obtained as the sum of products of elements in a row of the first matrix $[Z]$ by the corresponding element in a column of the second matrix $[C]$. If $[K]$ is written as

$$[K] = \begin{array}{|c|c|} \hline K_{11} & K_{12} \\ \hline K_{21} & K_{22} \\ \hline K_{31} & K_{32} \\ \hline \end{array} \qquad \ldots(11.10)$$

then

$$K_{rs} = \sum_n (Z_{rn} C_{ns}). \qquad \ldots(11.11)$$

The rules of matrix multiplication apply also to the product shown on the right-hand side of Eqn. (11.2). The original equations (11.1) are obtained from Eqn. (11.2) by evaluating the matrix product in accordance with the rule stated above.

Several conditions must be complied with if two matrices are to be multiplied together. For a fuller discussion of the methods of matrix algebra the reader should refer to a textbook such as Ref. 46.1.

### Transformation of an impedance matrix

If in addition to the transformation of the currents the voltages $e_1$, $e_2$, $e_3$ are transformed to new voltages $e_1'$, $e_2'$, the relation between the transformed voltage matrix $[e']$ and the transformed current matrix $[i']$ is given by a relation

$$[e'] = [Z'] . [i'], \qquad \ldots(11.12)$$

where $[Z']$ is a transformed impedance matrix.

If the voltage transformation is given by

$$\begin{array}{|c|} \hline e_1' \\ \hline e_2' \\ \hline \end{array} = \begin{array}{|c|c|c|} \hline B_{11} & B_{12} & B_{13} \\ \hline B_{21} & B_{22} & B_{23} \\ \hline \end{array} \cdot \begin{array}{|c|} \hline e_1 \\ \hline e_2 \\ \hline e_3 \\ \hline \end{array} \qquad \ldots(11.13)$$

or $$[e']=[B].[e], \qquad \qquad ...(11.14)$$

then $$[e']=[B].[Z].[C].[i'],$$

hence $$Z'=[B].[Z].[C]. \qquad \qquad ...(11.15)$$

Thus the new impedance matrix is obtained by two successive matrix multiplications, which must be performed in a certain order.

### Invariance of power

It should be noted that the two matrices $[B]$ and $[C]$ are of a different form in that $[B]$ transforms the new voltages into the old voltages, whereas $[C]$ transforms the old currents into the new currents. From the mathematical point of view the two transformation matrices may be quite independent of each other. In a physical problem, however, the variables have a physical meaning and there are restrictions on the manner in which they can be transformed. For electrical machines and circuits the total power is a definite quantity in ordinary units, however the voltages and currents are expressed. If, however, the change of variables is associated with a change of units, the coefficient $k_p$ in Eqn. (2.5) may be different for the two systems of description. If the transformation is such that the same coefficient is used,

$$P=k_p\Sigma(ei)=k_p\Sigma(e'i'). \qquad \qquad ...(11.16)$$

The power is then said to be *invariant* under the transformation.

If this condition holds there is a simple relation between the voltage transformation matrix $[B]$ and the current transformation matrix $[C]$. In the above example,

$$e_1i_1+e_2i_2+e_3i_3=e_1'i_1'+e_2'i_2'.$$

If now $i_1$, $i_2$, $i_3$ are substituted from Eqns. (11.4) in the left-hand side, and $e_1'$, $e_2'$ from Eqns. (11.13) in the right-hand side,

$$C_{11}e_1i_1'+C_{12}e_1i_2'+C_{21}e_2i_1'+C_{22}e_2i_2'+C_{31}e_3i_1'+C_{32}e_3i_2'$$
$$\equiv B_{11}e_1i_1'+B_{12}e_2i_1'+B_{13}e_3i_1'+B_{21}e_1i_2'+B_{22}e_2i_2'+B_{23}e_2i_3'.$$

The identity is true for all values of $e_1$, $e_2$, $e_3$, $i_1'$, $i_2'$. Hence

$$[B]=[C_t], \qquad \qquad ...(11.17)$$

where $[C_t]$ is the *transpose* of the matrix $[C]$. The transpose of a matrix is obtained by interchanging corresponding rows and columns. Thus the elements of the $n$th column of $[C_t]$ are the same as the elements of the $n$th row of $[C]$, or

$$(C_t)_{rs}=C_{sr}.$$

The result is evidently valid for matrices with any numbers of rows and columns. Hence if it is known that the power is invariant, it is only necessary to determine the current transformation matrix $[C]$. The voltage transformation matrix is $[C_t]$ and the transformed impedance matrix is given by

$$[Z']=[C_t].[Z].[C]. \qquad \qquad ...(11.18)$$

*Connection matrices*

For an electrical network or system consisting of inter-connected branches, the derivation of the equations is often a tedious process. They may be obtained in a simpler and better

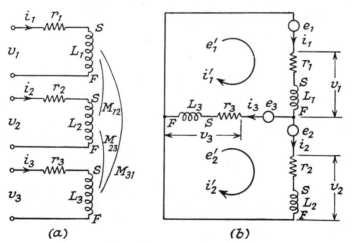

Fig. 60.—Transformation of a simple network.
(a) The primitive network.      (b) The actual network.

organised manner if equations are first written down for the separate branches, and then transformed by means of a transformation which takes into account the method of interconnection. The method can be used for systems, including machines as well as static elements, but the explanation below is given for a simple system of mutually coupled coils.

Fig. 60($a$) shows three coils with no electrical interconnections. The resistance, total self-inductance, applied voltage and current of each coil are denoted by $r$, $L$, $v$, $i$, with successive suffixes 1, 2, 3. The mutual inductances are $M_{23}$, $M_{31}$, $M_{12}$. The letters $S$ and $F$ indicate the start and finish of each coil in relation to a definite direction of winding. The operational equations of the system are then stated by the matrix equation

$$[v]=[Z].[i], \qquad \qquad ...(11.19)$$

where

$$[Z]= \begin{array}{|c|c|c|} \hline r_1+L_1p & M_{12}p & M_{31}p \\ \hline M_{12}p & r_2+L_2p & M_{23}p \\ \hline M_{31}p & M_{23}p & r_3+L_3p \\ \hline \end{array} \qquad ...(11.20)$$

Suppose now that the three coils are interconnected as shown in Fig. 60($b$), with voltages $e_1$, $e_2$, $e_3$ in series with the coils. The interconnection imposes a constraint such that only two currents are required to define the current distribution; for example, the mesh currents $i_1'$, $i_2'$. The new currents are related to the old currents by the matrix equation

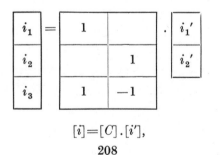

or $$[i]=[C].[i'], \qquad \qquad ...(11.21)$$

where

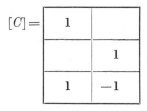

$$[C] = \qquad \dots(11.22)$$

is called a *connection matrix*.

If the mesh voltages $e_1$, $e_2$ are taken as the new voltage variables it is known that the power is invariant under this transformation. Hence the result of the last section can be used:

$$[e'] = [Z'] \cdot [i'], \qquad \dots(11.23)$$

where

$$[Z'] = [C_t] \cdot [Z] \cdot [C]. \qquad \dots(11.18)$$

The fact that the voltage transformation matrix is the transpose of the current transformation matrix can be readily verified from Fig. 60(b), since

$$e_1' = e_1 + e_3 = v_1 + v_3,$$
$$e_2' = e_2 - e_3 = v_2 - v_3,$$

or

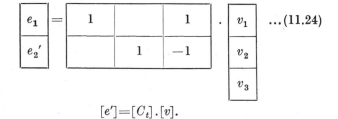

$$\dots(11.24)$$

$$[e'] = [C_t] \cdot [v].$$

The method is valid for any manner of interconnection of any number of branches, and provides a convenient means of deriving the equations of an electrical network or system.

1. Write down the impedance matrix $[Z]$ for a 'primitive' network with each branch taken separately.

209

2. Write down the connection matrix $[C]$ for the particular manner of interconnection.

3. Obtain the new impedance matrix $[Z']$ from Eqn. (11.18), using two successive matrix multiplications.

*Impedance matrix for A.C. circuits*

When complex number equations are used for A.C. circuits a modification is necessary, because the formula for power is different. The complex power is still invariant, but it is given by:

$$P + jQ = k_p \Sigma(\mathbf{E^*I}), \qquad \ldots(11.25)$$

using bold capital letters for the complex numbers representing the alternating voltages and currents. Hence if they are related by the matrix equation

$$[\mathbf{E}] = [Z] . [\mathbf{I}]$$

and the currents are transformed by:

$$[\mathbf{I}] = [C] . [\mathbf{I'}],$$

where the elements of $[Z]$ and $[C]$ may be complex, the transformed impedance is given by:

$$[Z'] = [C_t{}^*] . [Z] . [C]. \qquad \ldots(11.26)$$

The connection matrix in Eqn. (11.22) would not be affected by this modification, because it does not contain any complex elements, but some complex transformations are used later.

*Other transformations*

The later sections contain examples of other kinds of transformation. For some of the transformations the power is not invariant, and Eqn. (11.18) cannot be used without the inclusion of a special factor.

It may be noted that, for the transformation from phase to axis quantities stated by Eqns. (6.4) and (6.1), the power is not invariant, since its value is given by Eqns. (6.5) and (6.6), which contain different numerical coefficients. The reason for the difference, as explained on page 102, is that the unit of current for the axis currents is different from the unit for the phase currents.

210

### 44. Applications of the Generalised Equations of a Machine with Three Coils

In order to illustrate the wide range of application of the generalised theory some simple examples, based on the idealised diagram shown in Fig. 61, are discussed in this section. For a

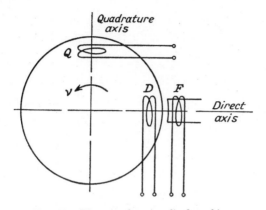

Fig. 61.—Diagram of a generalised machine represented by three coils.

machine represented by the two armature coils $D$ and $Q$, and the field coil $F$ of Fig. 61, the operational impedance matrix is:

|       | $f$ | $d$ | $q$ |
|-------|------|------|------|
| $Z=f$ | $r_f+L_fp$ | $L_{md}p$ | |
| $d$ | $L_{md}p$ | $r_a+L_dp$ | $L_qv$ |
| $q$ | $-L_{md}v$ | $-L_dv$ | $r_a+L_qp$ |

...(11.27)

and the electrical torque is

$$f = k_p\omega[L_{md}i_fi_q+(L_d-L_q)i_di_q].\qquad ...(11.28)$$

The letters $f$, $d$ and $q$ are shown opposite the rows and columns of the matrix $Z$ in order to indicate the variables to which they refer.

211

### D.C. machine

The equations apply directly to a cross-field generator having the three circuits shown in Fig. 62. They can be used for the simple D.C. machine with one armature circuit only, if circuit $D$ is omitted.

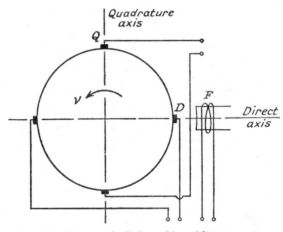

Fig. 62.—Diagram of a D.C. machine with two armature circuits and one field circuit.

### Synchronous machine

The equations contain the fictitious axis voltages and currents, and a transformation is necessary in order to obtain the phase values. Thus although the equations are the same as those of the D.C. machine a different interpretation is needed.

### D.C. machine with displaced brushes

Fig. 63 shows a D.C. machine with one set of brushes, denoted by $A$, displaced from the direct axis by an angle $\alpha$. The impedance matrix may be obtained from Eqns. (11.27) by means of a simple transformation.

The currents in Fig. 63 produce the same M.M.F. as those in Fig. 61 if

$$i_d = i_a \cos \alpha,$$
$$i_q = i_a \sin \alpha.$$

Hence the transformation is given by:

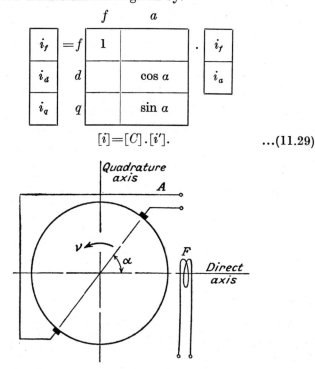

$$\begin{array}{c} \\ \\ \end{array} \quad \begin{array}{cc} f & a \end{array}$$

|  |  | $f$ | $a$ |
|---|---|---|---|
| $i_f$ | $=f$ | 1 |  |
| $i_d$ | $d$ |  | $\cos \alpha$ |
| $i_q$ | $q$ |  | $\sin \alpha$ |

$$\cdot \begin{array}{|c|} \hline i_f \\ \hline i_a \\ \hline \end{array}$$

or $\qquad [i]=[C].[i'].$ $\qquad \ldots(11.29)$

FIG. 63.—Diagram of a D.C. machine with displaced brushes, or of a repulsion motor.

$[C]$ is a connection matrix which can be used to transform the equations. Since the power is invariant the new impedance matrix is

$$[Z']=[C_t].[Z].[C].$$

To evaluate $[Z']$ first obtain $[Z].[C]$ as a matrix product.

$$[Z].[C]=$$

| $r_f+L_f p$ | $L_{md}p \cos \alpha$ |
|---|---|
| $L_{md}p$ | $(r_a+L_a p) \cos \alpha + L_q v \sin \alpha$ |
| $-L_{md}v$ | $-L_d v \cos \alpha + (r_a+L_q p) \sin \alpha$ |

213

The transpose of $[C]$ is

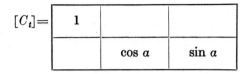

$$[C_t] = \begin{array}{|c|c|c|} \hline 1 & & \\ \hline & \cos \alpha & \sin \alpha \\ \hline \end{array}$$

A second matrix multiplication then gives

$$[Z'] = [C_t] . [Z] . [C]$$

$$= \begin{array}{|c|c|} \hline r_f + L_f p & L_{md} p \cos \alpha \\ \hline L_{md}(p \cos \alpha - \nu \sin \alpha) & \begin{array}{c} r_a + L_d p \cos^2 \alpha + L_q p \sin^2 \alpha \\ -(L_d - L_q)\nu \sin \alpha \cos \alpha \end{array} \\ \hline \end{array}$$

$$\ldots(11.30)$$

*Repulsion motor*

Fig. 63 is also the diagram of a repulsion motor, and the same equations hold. The repulsion motor differs from a D.C. machine in the following respects:

1. An alternating voltage is applied to the stator winding and the brushes are short-circuited.
2. The air-gap is uniform, hence $L_d = L_q = L_a$ (say).
3. The angle $\alpha$ is varied over a wide range in order to control the characteristics. (In the D.C. machine $\alpha$ is nearly 90°.)

The operational impedance matrix in Eqn. (11.30) simplifies to:

$$[Z'] = \begin{array}{|c|c|} \hline r_f + L_f p & L_{md} p \cos \alpha \\ \hline L_{md}(p \cos \alpha - \nu \sin \alpha) & r_a + L_a p \\ \hline \end{array} \quad \ldots(11.31)$$

During steady operation the supply voltage alternates at frequency $\omega/2\pi$, and the speed is constant. The vector equations are obtained by replacing $p$ by $j\omega$, and introducing the complex numbers representing the voltages and currents as explained on page 42. Let the speed be $\nu=v\omega$, where $v$ is a constant.

$$
\mathbf{E} =
\begin{array}{|c|c|}
\hline
r_f+jX_f & jX_m \cos \alpha \\
\hline
jX_m(\cos \alpha - v \sin \alpha) & r_a+jX_a \\
\hline
\end{array}
\cdot
\begin{array}{|c|}
\hline
\mathbf{I}_f \\
\hline
\mathbf{I}_a \\
\hline
\end{array}
\qquad \ldots(11.32)
$$

where $X_m=\omega L_{md}$, $X_f=\omega L_f$, $X_a=\omega L_a$.

The mean torque is given by:

$$
\begin{aligned}
F_e &= k_p \omega Re\{L_{md}\mathbf{I}_f\mathbf{I}_a{}^*\} \\
&= k_p Re\{X_m\mathbf{I}_f\mathbf{I}_a{}^* \sin \alpha\}.
\end{aligned}
\qquad \ldots(11.33)
$$

*Balanced polyphase operation of a synchronous machine*

For the normal steady operation of a synchronous machine, $i_f$, $i_d$, $i_q$, $e_f$, $e_d$, $e_q$ are all D.C. quantities, and the equations become, putting $p=0$, and $\nu=\omega$:

$$
\begin{array}{|c|}
\hline
e_f \\
\hline
e_d \\
\hline
e_q \\
\hline
\end{array}
=
\begin{array}{|c|c|c|}
\hline
r_f & & \\
\hline
& r_a & x_q \\
\hline
-x_{md} & -x_d & r_a \\
\hline
\end{array}
\cdot
\begin{array}{|c|}
\hline
i_f \\
\hline
i_d \\
\hline
i_q \\
\hline
\end{array}
\qquad \ldots(11.34)
$$

It has been shown in Sect. 28 that the complex numbers representing the phase voltages and currents are:

$$
\mathbf{E}=\frac{1}{\sqrt{2}}(e_d-je_q)=\mathbf{E}_d+\mathbf{E}_q,
$$

$$
\mathbf{I}=\frac{1}{\sqrt{2}}(i_d-ji_q)=\mathbf{I}_d+\mathbf{I}_q.
$$

By combining the second and third equations (11.34) and substituting $i_d = \sqrt{2}\mathbf{I}_d$, $i_q = \sqrt{2}j\mathbf{I}_q$, the equations become:

$$\begin{array}{|c|} e_f \\ \hline E \end{array} = \begin{array}{|c|c|c|} r_f & & \\ \hline \dfrac{j}{\sqrt{2}}x_{md} & r_a+jx_d & r_a+jx_q \end{array} \cdot \begin{array}{|c|} i_f \\ \hline \mathbf{I}_d \\ \hline \mathbf{I}_q \end{array} \qquad \ldots(11.35)$$

For a cylindrical rotor machine, with $x_d = x_q$, the equations simplify further to:

$$\begin{array}{|c|} e_f \\ \hline E \end{array} = \begin{array}{|c|c|} r_f & \\ \hline \dfrac{j}{\sqrt{2}}x_{md} & r_a+jx_d \end{array} \cdot \begin{array}{|c|} i_f \\ \hline \mathbf{I} \end{array} \qquad \ldots(11.36)$$

## 45. Steady-state Equations of the Polyphase Induction Motor and the Schrage Motor

*The polyphase induction motor*

For A.C. operation at slip $s$, Eqns. (6.32) become:

$$\begin{array}{|c|} \mathbf{E}_{d1} \\ \hline \mathbf{E}_{d2} \\ \hline \mathbf{E}_{q2} \\ \hline \mathbf{E}_{q1} \end{array} = \begin{array}{|c|c|c|c|} r_1+jX_1 & jX_m & & \\ \hline jX_m & r_2+jX_2 & (1-s)X_2 & (1-s)X_m \\ \hline -(1-s)X_m & -(1-s)X_2 & r_2+jX_2 & jX_m \\ \hline & & jX_m & r_1+jX_1 \end{array} \cdot \begin{array}{|c|} \mathbf{I}_{d1} \\ \hline \mathbf{I}_{d2} \\ \hline \mathbf{I}_{q2} \\ \hline \mathbf{I}_{q1} \end{array}$$

$$\ldots(11.37)$$

or $$[\mathbf{E}] = [Z] \cdot [\mathbf{I}].$$

During balanced polyphase operation each pair of axis currents forms a two-phase system, the quadrature-axis currents lagging behind the direct-axis currents. Hence

$$\mathbf{I}_{d1} = j\mathbf{I}_{q1} = \mathbf{I}_1 \text{ (say)},$$
$$\mathbf{I}_{d2} = j\mathbf{I}_{q2} = \mathbf{I}_2.$$

These relations can be expressed in terms of a transformation matrix $[C]$, which transforms the four old currents $\mathbf{I}_{d1}$, $\mathbf{I}_{d2}$, $\mathbf{I}_{q1}$, $\mathbf{I}_{q2}$ into two new currents $\mathbf{I}_1$, $\mathbf{I}_2$.

$$\begin{array}{c} \mathbf{I}_{d1} \\ \mathbf{I}_{d2} \\ \mathbf{I}_{q2} \\ \mathbf{I}_{q1} \end{array} = \begin{array}{|cc|} \hline 1 & \\ & 1 \\ & -j \\ -j & \\ \hline \end{array} \cdot \begin{array}{c} \mathbf{I}_1 \\ \mathbf{I}_2 \end{array} \qquad \text{...(11.38)}$$

or $\qquad\qquad [\mathbf{I}] = [C] \cdot [\mathbf{I}'].$

For the above transformation the power is not invariant, since a factor 2 must be introduced to allow for the reduction in the number of circuits. The power equation is:

$$P + jQ = k_p \Sigma(\mathbf{EI}^*) = 2k_p \Sigma(\mathbf{E'I'}^*). \qquad \text{...(11.39)}$$

Hence the transformed impedance matrix is:

$$[Z'] = \tfrac{1}{2}[C_t{}^*] \cdot [Z] \cdot [C].$$

Evaluating $[Z']$ by two successive matrix multiplications, the well-known steady-state equations of the polyphase induction motor are obtained.

$$\begin{array}{c} \mathbf{E}_1 \\ \mathbf{E}_2 \end{array} = \begin{array}{|cc|} \hline r_1 + jX_1 & jX_m \\ jsX_m & r_2 + jsX_2 \\ \hline \end{array} \cdot \begin{array}{c} \mathbf{I}_1 \\ \mathbf{I}_2 \end{array} \qquad \text{...(11.40)}$$

If per-unit values of the quantities are used, $k_p = \tfrac{1}{2}$, as in Eqn. (6.6). Hence the motoring torque is given by:

$$\begin{aligned} F_m &= \tfrac{1}{2}X_m Re\{\mathbf{I}_{d2}{}^* \mathbf{I}_{q1} - \mathbf{I}_{d1}{}^* \mathbf{I}_{q2}\} \\ &= X_m Re\{j\mathbf{I}_1 \mathbf{I}_2{}^*\}. \qquad \text{...(11.41)} \end{aligned}$$

*The Schrage motor*

The Schrage motor has three polyphase windings, illustrated in Fig. 64, in which all the windings are three-phase.

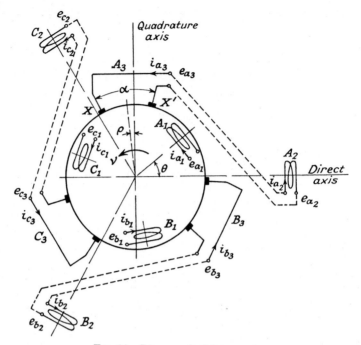

FIG. 64.—Diagram of a Schrage motor.

1. Three-phase primary winding on the rotor (coils $A1$, $B1$, $C1$), supplied at line frequency.
2. Three-phase secondary winding on the stator (coils $A2$, $B2$, $C2$).
3. A commutator winding on the rotor with three pairs of movable brushes (circuits $A3$, $B3$, $C3$). The brush setting is defined by the angular separation $\alpha$ between brushes $X$ and $X'$ of the same phase, and the angle of shift $\varrho$ between the mid-point of $XX'$ and the quadrature axis. If $\varrho=0$, the axis of the M.M.F. wave set up by a current in the circuit $A3$ is along the direct axis.

Windings 2 and 3 are connected together as shown by the dotted lines, so that the commutator winding provides the injected voltage required for regulating the induction motor, of which winding 1 is the primary and winding 2 the secondary.

Each of the three polyphase windings can be replaced by a pair of coils on the axes as indicated by the generalised diagram (Fig. 65). The derivation of the equations for steady operation is carried out in three stages:

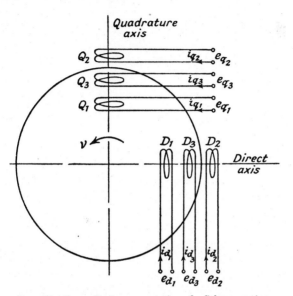

FIG. 65.—Generalised representation of a Schrage motor.

1. Write down the equations of the generalised machine of Fig. 65, treating each of the six coils separately.
2. Transform into three new equations, which apply for the condition of balanced polyphase operation.
3. Transform again to take into account the interconnection between the secondary and commutator windings, thus reducing the number of equations to two.

The machine is assumed to run steadily in the forward direction at a speed $(1-s)\omega$, where $s$ is the slip. The phase sequence of the applied voltages on the primary winding is $A-B-C$, causing the flux to rotate backwards relative to the primary winding. When the circuits are transformed into those shown in Fig. 65, the voltages and currents all alternate at slip frequency. Hence $p$ must be replaced by $js\omega$, and the equations are:

| $\mathbf{E}_{d1}$ | $=$ | $r_1+js\omega L_1$ | $js\omega M_{12}$ | $js\omega M_{31}$ | $(1-s)\omega M_{31}$ | $(1-s)\omega M_{12}$ | $(1-s)\omega L_1$ |
|---|---|---|---|---|---|---|---|
| $\mathbf{E}_{d2}$ | | $js\omega M_{12}$ | $r_2+js\omega L_2$ | $js\omega M_{23}$ | | | |
| $\mathbf{E}_{d3}$ | | $js\omega M_{31}$ | $js\omega M_{23}$ | $r_3+js\omega L_3$ | $(1-s)\omega L_3$ | $(1-s)\omega M_{23}$ | $(1-s)\omega M_{31}$ |
| $\mathbf{E}_{q3}$ | | $-(1-s)\omega M_{31}$ | $-(1-s)\omega M_{23}$ | $-(1-s)\omega L_3$ | $r_3+js\omega L_3$ | $js\omega M_{23}$ | $js\omega M_{31}$ |
| $\mathbf{E}_{q2}$ | | | | | $js\omega M_{23}$ | $r_2+js\omega L_2$ | $js\omega M_{12}$ |
| $\mathbf{E}_{q1}$ | | $-(1-s)\omega L_1$ | $-(1-s)\omega M_{12}$ | $-(1-s)\omega M_{31}$ | $js\omega M_{31}$ | $js\omega M_{12}$ | $r_1+js\omega L_1$ |

$$\dots(11$$

or
$$[\mathbf{E}]=[Z] \cdot [\mathbf{I}].$$

The impedance matrix contains three self-inductances $L_1$, $L_2$, $L_3$, and three mutual inductances $M_{23}$, $M_{31}$, $M_{12}$. The values of these coefficients can be found in terms of the normal magnetising and leakage reactances by considering the fluxes linking the three windings. Fig. 66 is a diagram in which each winding is represented by a single conductor. The commutator winding occupies the top of the rotor slot. If the quantities in the equations are per-unit values, each of the four fluxes shown corresponds to a mutual reactance or a leakage reactance, the value of which at a given frequency can be calculated by normal design methods. The reactances given below are all at supply frequency.

$\Phi$ is the main flux linking all windings and corresponds to the magnetising reactance $X_m$.

$\Phi_1$, $\Phi_2$, $\Phi_3$ are leakage fluxes corresponding to leakage reactances $x_1, x_2, x_3$.

It is assumed that there is no leakage flux linking winding 3 only. Thus the leakage flux $\Phi_3$ links winding 1 as well as winding 3.

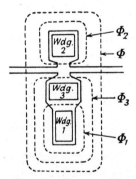

Fig. 66.—Diagram of the fluxes in a Schrage motor.

With these assumptions the mutual reactances $\omega M_{12}$ and $\omega M_{23}$ are both equal to $X_m$, and $\omega M_{31}$ equals $(X_m + x_3)$. Each of the self-reactances $\omega L_1$, $\omega L_2$, $\omega L_3$ is the sum of $X_m$ and the appropriate leakage reactance. Thus

$$\omega M_{23} = X_m \qquad \omega L_1 = X_m + x_1,$$
$$\omega M_{31} = X_m + x_3 \qquad \omega L_2 = X_m + x_2,$$
$$\omega M_{12} = X_m \qquad \omega L_3 = X_m + x_3.$$

*Transformation matrix for polyphase operation*

During steady balanced polyphase operation each pair of axis currents forms a two-phase system, as in the induction motor. In the Schrage motor, however, as already explained, the rotating flux moves backwards when $s$ is positive, and hence the quadrature-axis current leads the direct-axis current.

$$\mathbf{I}_{d1} = -j\mathbf{I}_{q1} = \mathbf{I}_1 \text{ (say)},$$
$$\mathbf{I}_{d2} = -j\mathbf{I}_{q2} = \mathbf{I}_2,$$
$$\mathbf{I}_{d3} = -j\mathbf{I}_{q3} = \mathbf{I}_3.$$

In matrix form:

$$
\begin{bmatrix} \mathbf{I}_{d1} \\ \mathbf{I}_{d2} \\ \mathbf{I}_{d3} \\ \mathbf{I}_{q3} \\ \mathbf{I}_{q2} \\ \mathbf{I}_{q1} \end{bmatrix}
=
\begin{bmatrix} 1 & & \\ & 1 & \\ & & 1 \\ & & j \\ & j & \\ j & & \end{bmatrix}
\cdot
\begin{bmatrix} \mathbf{I}_1 \\ \mathbf{I}_2 \\ \mathbf{I}_3 \end{bmatrix}
\qquad \ldots(11.43)
$$

or

$$[\mathbf{I}] = [C] \cdot [\mathbf{I'}].$$

The new impedance matrix is:

$$[Z'] = \tfrac{1}{2}[C_t{}^*] \cdot [Z] \cdot [C],$$

and the new equations are:

$$\begin{bmatrix} \mathbf{E}_1 \\ \mathbf{E}_2 \\ \mathbf{E}_3 \end{bmatrix} = \begin{bmatrix} r_1+j(X_m+x_1) & jX_m & j(X_m+x_3) \\ jsX_m & r_2+js(X_m+x_2) & jsX_m \\ j(X_m+x_3) & jX_m & r_3+j(X_m+x_3) \end{bmatrix} \cdot \begin{bmatrix} \mathbf{I}_1 \\ \mathbf{I}_2 \\ \mathbf{I}_3 \end{bmatrix}$$

$$\dots(11.44)$$

*Connection matrix*

The fact that the windings 2 and 3 are connected in opposition means that the actual phase currents (not the per-unit values) are equal and opposite. Thus if $\mathbf{I}_{a2}$ and $\mathbf{I}_{a3}$ are the per-unit phase currents, and $r$ is the ratio of effective turns of winding 3 to winding 2, then

$$r\mathbf{I}_{a2}=-\mathbf{I}_{a3}.$$

The relation between phase and axis currents for winding 2, with phase $A2$ located on the direct axis, is given by Eqns. (6.31) with $i_0=0$. Hence

$$\mathbf{I}_{a2}=\mathbf{I}_{d2}.$$

The transformation equation for winding 3, with phase $A3$ located at an angle $\varrho$ from the direct axis, is

$$\mathbf{I}_{a3}=\mathbf{I}_{d3}\cos\varrho+\mathbf{I}_{q3}\sin\varrho=\mathbf{I}_3\varepsilon^{-j\varrho}.$$

The transformation equations are therefore:

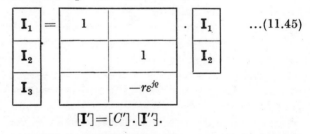

$$\dots(11.45)$$

or
$$[\mathbf{I}']=[C'].[\mathbf{I}''].$$

For this connection transformation the power is invariant, and the final impedance matrix is:

$$[Z'']=[C_t'^*].[Z'].[C'].$$

The applied voltages are $\mathbf{E}$ in the primary circuit and zero in

222

the combined secondary circuit. Hence the equations of the Schrage motor are:

$$
\mathbf{E} =
\begin{vmatrix}
r_1 + j(X_m + x_1) & jX_m - j(X_m + x_3)r\varepsilon^{-j\varrho} \\
jsX_m - j(X_m + x_3)r\varepsilon^{-j\varrho} & \begin{matrix} r_2 + j(sx_2 + r^2x_3) \\ + jX_m(s - sr\varepsilon^{-j\varrho} + r^2 - r\varepsilon^{j\varrho}) \end{matrix}
\end{vmatrix}
\cdot
\begin{vmatrix}
\mathbf{I}_1 \\
\mathbf{I}_2
\end{vmatrix}
$$

...(11.46)

The motoring torque is obtained from the rotation voltage terms of Eqns. (11.42), and can be simplified by using the current relations in Eqns. (11.43) and (11.45):

$$
\begin{aligned}
F_m = & -\frac{\omega}{2} Re\{\mathbf{I}_{d1}*(L_1\mathbf{I}_{q1} + M_{12}\mathbf{I}_{q2} + M_{31}\mathbf{I}_{q3}) \\
& + \mathbf{I}_{d3}*(M_{31}\mathbf{I}_{q1} + M_{23}\mathbf{I}_{q2} + L_3\mathbf{I}_{q3}) \\
& - \mathbf{I}_{q1}*(L_1\mathbf{I}_{d1} + M_{12}\mathbf{I}_{d2} + M_{31}\mathbf{I}_{d3}) \\
& + \mathbf{I}_{q3}*(M_{31}\mathbf{I}_{d1} + M_{23}\mathbf{I}_{d2} + L_3\mathbf{I}_{d3})\} \\
= & \ Re\{jX_m\mathbf{I}_2*(\mathbf{I}_1 - \mathbf{I}_2r\varepsilon^{-j\varrho})\}.
\end{aligned}
$$
...(11.47)

The result agrees with that obtained by different methods in Refs. 46.3 and 51.5.

### 46. The Equations of Interconnected Systems

All the examples given so far have related to single machines for which the external conditions are specified. Often, however, two or more machines are connected together in such a way that each affects the action of the other. For such combinations the system must be considered as a whole, and it is necessary to derive a combined set of equations in which the variables are all the independent currents of the complete system and all the independent speeds. The source voltages and the impressed torques corresponding to the currents and speeds also appear in the equations. The system equations can be conveniently derived by first obtaining the equations of each component separately and then combining them together by means of a connection matrix.

In a system containing D.C. machines, for which the currents in the equations are the actual currents in the external circuits, the process is no more complicated than for a static network.

With A.C. machines, where the axis currents in the equations are related to the external currents by a transformation, the conditions may be much more difficult. In the following pages the method is explained by means of two simple examples, one giving a general analysis of a D.C. machine system, and the second a limited analysis, applicable only to steady operation, for an A.C. machine system.

*Amplidyne voltage regulator system*

A simple voltage regulating system, comprising an amplidyne, a D.C. generator, and a stabilising transformer, is shown in

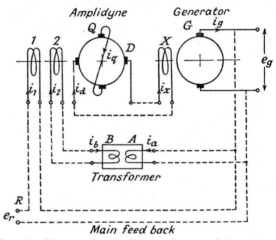

FIG. 67.—Diagram of an amplidyne voltage regulating system.

Fig. 67. The amplidyne, which excites the generator, has two field windings, one of which provides the normal excitation while the other is used for stabilising in conjunction with the transformer. The three component machines are shown by full lines while the interconnections between them are shown dotted, and each circuit is denoted by a letter which serves as a suffix. The output voltage $e_g$ of the generator is fed back to the main amplidyne field winding in series with a reference voltage $e_r$. The equations are derived for the condition when the generator is open-circuited.

The overall impedance matrix for the circuits of the component machines treated separately is obtained by combining the three matrices of the separate machines, as indicated in Eqns. (11.48) by the heavy lines. The drop in the generator armature due to the small current $i_g$ is neglected, and hence there are no coefficients in the last column of the matrix.

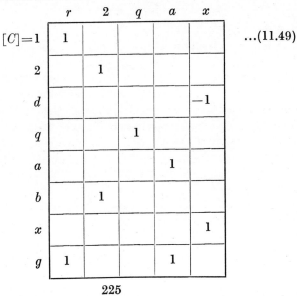

|  | 1 | 2 | d | q | a | b | x | g |
|---|---|---|---|---|---|---|---|---|
| $[Z]=1$ | $r_1+L_1p$ | $M_{12}p$ |  |  |  |  |  |  |
| 2 | $M_{12}p$ | $r_2+L_2p$ |  |  |  |  |  |  |
| d | $M_1p$ | $M_2p$ | $r_d+L_dp$ | $L_qv_a$ |  |  |  |  |
| q | $-M_1v_a$ | $-M_2v_a$ | $-L_dv_a$ | $r_q+L_qp$ |  |  |  |  |
| a |  |  |  |  | $r_a+L_ap$ | $Mp$ |  |  |
| b |  |  |  |  | $Mp$ | $r_b+L_bp$ |  |  |
| x |  |  |  |  |  |  | $r_x+L_xp$ |  |
| g |  |  |  |  |  |  | $-M_gv_g$ |  |

$$...(11.48)$$

The connection matrix is:

|  | r | 2 | q | a | x |
|---|---|---|---|---|---|
| $[C]=1$ | 1 |  |  |  |  |
| 2 |  | 1 |  |  |  |
| d |  |  |  |  | $-1$ |
| q |  |  | 1 |  |  |
| a |  |  |  | 1 |  |
| b |  | 1 |  |  |  |
| x |  |  |  |  | 1 |
| g | 1 |  |  | 1 |  |

$$...(11.49)$$

225

The new impedance matrix is therefore:

$$[Z']=[C_t].[Z].[C]$$

|   | $r$ | $2$ | $q$ | $a$ | $x$ |
|---|---|---|---|---|---|
| $=r$ | $r_1+L_1p$ | $M_{12}p$ | | | $M_gv_g$ |
| $2$ | $M_{12}p$ | $r_2+r_b+$ $(L_2+L_b)p$ | | $Mp$ | |
| $q$ | $-M_1v_a$ | $-M_2v_a$ | $r_q+L_qp$ | | $-L_dv_a$ |
| $a$ | | $Mp$ | | $r_a+L_ap$ | $M_gv_g$ |
| $x$ | $-M_1p$ | $-M_2p$ | $-L_qv_a$ | | $r_d+r_x+$ $(L_d+L_x)p$ |

$$...(11.50)$$

*Two induction motors used as power selsyns*

Figs. 68(*a*) and 68(*b*) are diagrams representing two power selsyns. The machines are ordinary induction motors with three-phase windings on both stator and rotor, for each of which only phase $A$ is shown. The primary windings $TA1$ and $RA1$ in Fig. 68(*a*) are connected to a common supply voltage **E**, and the secondary windings $TA2$ and $RA2$ are connected in opposition. Under steady conditions the two machines run in synchronism with each other at exactly the same speed, and operate as power selsyns, one being a transmitter and the other a receiver. The rotors run with the same slip $s$ and with a constant angular displacement $\delta$ between them. Thus if phase $TA2$ of the transmitter secondary winding has the angular position $\theta$ at the instant considered, the angle of phase $RA2$ of the receiver secondary winding is $\theta-\delta$.

The diagram of the corresponding generalised machines is shown in Fig. 68(*b*), in which only the direct-axis coils $T1$, $T2$,

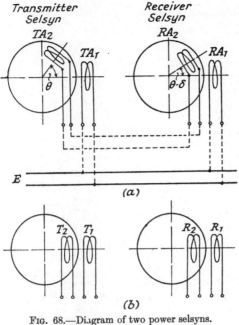

FIG. 68.—Diagram of two power selsyns.
(a) Phase diagram.  (b) Axis diagram.

$R1$, $R2$ are indicated. The impedance matrix, treating the four coils separately, is:

|  | $t1$ | $t2$ | $r1$ | $r2$ |
|---|---|---|---|---|
| $[Z]=t1$ | $r_{t1}+jX_{t1}$ | $jX_{tm}$ |  |  |
| $t2$ | $jsX_{tm}$ | $r_{t2}+jsX_{t2}$ |  |  |
| $r1$ |  |  | $r_{r1}+jX_{r1}$ | $jX_{rm}$ |
| $r2$ |  |  | $jsX_{rm}$ | $r_{r2}+jsX_{r2}$ |

$$...(11.51)$$

where $X$, with appropriate suffixes, denotes the complete self-reactances and the magnetising reactances of the two machines at supply frequency.

In order to allow for the secondary connection it is necessary

227

to obtain a relation between the currents $I_{t2}$ and $I_{r2}$. Because of the connection the actual secondary phase currents are equal and opposite. Hence if the windings of the two machines are identical the per-unit phase currents are related by:

$$I_{ta2} = -I_{ra2}.$$

Now for steady polyphase operation the axis currents are related by:

$$I_{td2} = jI_{tq2} = I_{t2},$$

and

$$I_{ta2} = I_{td2} \cos \theta + I_{tq2} \sin \theta$$
$$= I_{t2} \varepsilon^{-j\theta}.$$

Similarly

$$I_{ra2} = I_{r2} \varepsilon^{-j(\theta - \delta)}.$$

Hence

$$I_{t2} = -\varepsilon^{j} I_{r2}.$$

The connection matrix is therefore the following:

|          | t1 | r1 | 2 |
|----------|----|----|----|
| $[C] = t1$ | 1  |    |    |
| $t2$     |    |    | 1  |
| $r1$     |    | 1  |    |
| $r2$     |    |    | $-\varepsilon^{-j\delta}$ |

...(11.52)

and the combined impedance matrix is:

$$[Z'] = [C_t{}^*] . [Z] . [C].$$

The equations of the system are therefore:

| $E$ | = | $r_{t1} + jX_{t1}$ |                            | $jX_{tm}$                          | . | $I_{t1}$ |
|-----|---|--------------------|----------------------------|------------------------------------|---|----------|
| $E$ |   |                    | $r_{r1} + jX_{r1}$         | $-jX_{rm}\varepsilon^{-j\delta}$   |   | $I_{r1}$ |
|     |   | $jsX_{tm}$         | $-jsX_{rm}\varepsilon^{j\delta}$ | $r_{t1} + r_{r2} + js(X_{t2} + X_{r2})$ |   | $I_2$    |

...(11.53)

## *More difficult problems*

In order to explain the method clearly and briefly two very simple examples have been given. These examples, as well as those discussed earlier in the chapter, show how the algebraic substitutions required to transform from one set of variables to another can be carried out by means of matrix multiplication. The process is in fact so clear that, for anyone not very familiar with matrix methods, it would be easier, for any of the simple examples considered, to use the ordinary algebraic methods. For more complicated problems, for which the ordinary algebraic manipulations may become very involved, the advantages of the matrix method become more evident. The subject is treated fully in Refs. 42.1 and 51.6, to which the present discussion is only an introduction.

# CHRONOLOGICAL BIBLIOGRAPHY

*(The reference numbers denote year of publication.)*

| *Ref. No.* | *Book or Paper* | *Page* |
|---|---|---|
| 23.1 | DOHERTY, R. E. "A Simplified Method of Analysing Short-circuit Problems." *Trans. A.I.E.E.*, 1923, vol. 42, page 841. | 182 |
| 26.1 | WEST, H. R. "Cross-field Theory of Alternating Current Machines." *Trans. A.I.E.E.*, 1926, vol. 45, page 466. | 3 |
| 26.2 | DOHERTY, R. E. and NICKLE, C. A. "Synchronous Machines I. An Extension of Blondel's Two-Reaction Theory." *Trans. A.I.E.E.*, 1926, vol. 45, page 912. | 3 |
| 26.3 | DOHERTY, R. E. and NICKLE, C. A. "Synchronous Machines II. Steady Power Angle Characteristics." *Trans. A.I.E.E.*, 1926, vol. 45, page 927. | 3 |
| 27.1 | DOHERTY, R. E. and NICKLE, C. A. "Synchronous Machines III. Torque Angle Characteristics under Transient Conditions." *Trans. A.I.E.E.*, 1927, vol. 46, page 1. | 3, 166 |
| 28.1 | DOHERTY, R. E. and NICKLE, C. A. "Synchronous Machines IV. Single-Phase Short Circuits." *Trans. A.I.E.E.*, 1928, vol. 47, page 457. | 3, 187 |
| 28.2 | PARK, R. H. "Definition of an Ideal Synchronous Machine." *G.E. Review*, 1928, vol. 31, page 332. | 3, 22 |
| 29.1 | PARK, R. H. "Two-Reaction Theory of Synchronous Machines." *Trans. A.I.E.E.*, 1929, vol. 48, page 716. | 3 |
| 30.1 | LINVILLE, T. M. "Starting Performance of Salient-Pole Synchronous Machines." *Trans. A.I.E.E.*, 1930, vol. 49, page 531. | 140 |
| 30.2 | DOHERTY, R. E. and NICKLE, C. A. "Synchronous Machines V. Three-Phase Short Circuit." *Trans. A.I.E.E.*, 1930, vol. 49, page 700. | 3, 183 |
| 30.3 | WAGNER, C. F. "Effect of Armature Resistance on Hunting of Synchronous Machines." *Trans. A.I.E.E.*, 1930, vol. 49, page 1011. | 173 |
| 31.1 | KILGORE, L. A. "Calculation of Synchronous Machine Constants." *Trans. A.I.E.E.*, 1931, vol. 50, page 1201. | 122 |
| 31.2 | WRIGHT, S. H. "Determination of Synchronous Machine Constants by Test." *Trans. A.I.E.E.*, 1931, vol. 50, page 1331. | 122 |
| 33.1 | WAGNER, C. F. and EVANS, R. D. *Symmetrical Components* (book), McGraw-Hill, 1933. | 152 |
| 33.2 | PARK, R. H. "Two-Reaction Theory of Synchronous Machines II." *Trans. A.I.E.E.*, 1933, vol. 52, page 352. | 3 |

# CHRONOLOGICAL BIBLIOGRAPHY

| Ref. No. | Book or Paper | Page |
|---|---|---|
| 34.1 | LEWIS, W. A. "Quick Response Excitation." *Electric Journal*, 1934, vol. 31, page 308. | 77 |
| 34.2 | PRESCOTT, J. C. and RICHARDSON, J. E. "The Inherent Instability of Synchronous Machinery." *Jour. I.E.E.*, 1934, vol. 75, page 497. | 173 |
| 35.1 | KRON, G. "The Application of Tensors to the Analysis of Rotating Electrical Machinery." *G.E. Review*, 1935, vol. 36, page 181 *et seq.* | 3, 124 |
| 35.2 | KINGSLEY, C., JR. "Saturated Synchronous Reactance." *Trans. A.I.E.E.*, 1935, vol. 54, page 300. | 22, 175 |
| 35.3 | SHOULTS, D. R., CRARY, S. B. and LAUDER, A. H. "Pull-in Characteristics of Synchronous Motors." *Trans. A.I.E.E.*, 1935, vol. 54, page 1385. | 160 |
| 38.1 | STANLEY, H. C. "An Analysis of the Induction Machine." *Trans. A.I.E.E.*, 1938, vol. 57, page 751. | 124 |
| 40.1 | BOICE, W. K., CRARY, S. B., KRON, G. and THOMPSON, L. W. "The Direct-Acting Generator Voltage Regulator." *Trans. A.I.E.E.*, 1940, vol. 59, page 149. | 85 |
| 41.1 | *American Standard Definitions of Electrical Terms* (book). A.I.E.E. Publication, 1941. | 122, 182 |
| 42.1 | KRON, G. *Application of Tensors to the Analysis of Rotating Electrical Machinery* (book), *G.E. Review*, 1942. | 3, 5, 229 |
| 44.1 | CARTER, G. W. *Electrical Transients* (book), Cambridge Univ. Press, 1944. | 44 |
| 44.2 | WAGNER, C. F. *Machine Characteristics. Electrical Transmission and Distribution* (book), Chap. 7. Westinghouse Co. 1944. | 78 |
| 44.3 | MAGINESS, F. J. and SCHULTZ, N. R. "Transient Performance of an Induction Motor." *Trans. A.I.E.E.*, 1944, vol. 63, page 641. | 134 |
| 44.4 | HARDER, E. L. and CHEEK, R. C. "Regulation of A.C. Generators with Suddenly Applied Loads." *Trans. A.I.E.E.*, 1944, vol. 63, page 310. | 199 |
| 45.1 | CRARY, S. B. *Power System Stability*, Vol. I. *Steady State Stability* (book), John Wiley, 1945. | 193 |
| 45.2 | RANKIN, A. W. "The Direct and Quadrature Axis Equivalent Circuits of the Synchronous Machine." *Trans. A.I.E.E.*, 1945, vol. 64, page 861. | 115 |
| 45.3 | PETERSON, H. A. and CONCORDIA, C. "Analysers for use in Engineering and Scientific Problems." *G.E. Review*, 1945, vol. 48, page 29. | 51 |
| 45.4 | *A.I.E.E. Test Code for Synchronous Machines.* A.I.E.E. Publication No. 503, New York, 1945. | 122 |
| 46.1 | PIPES, L. A. *Applied Mathematics for Engineers and Physicists* (book), McGraw-Hill, 1946. | 205 |

| Ref. No. | Book or Paper | Page |
|---|---|---|
| 46.2 | LINVILLE, T. M. "Current and Torque of D.C. Machine on Short Circuit." *Trans. A.I.E.E.*, 1946, vol. 65, page 956. | 67 |
| 46.3 | GIBBS, W. J. "The Equations and Circle Diagrams of the Schrage Motor." *Jour. I.E.E.*, 1946, vol. 93, Part II, page 621. | 221–, 223 |
| 47.1 | CRARY, S. B. *Power System Stability*, Vol. 2. *Transient Stability* (book), John Wiley, 1947. | 193, 196 |
| 47.2 | ADKINS, B. "Amplidyne Regulating Systems." *Jour. I.E.E.*, 1947, vol. 94, Pt. IIA, page 49. | 78 |
| 49.1 | LINVILLE, T. M. and WARD, H. C. "Solid Short Circuit of D.C. Motors and Generators." *Trans. A.I.E.E.*, 1949, vol. 68, page 119. | 67 |
| 49.2 | DUESTERHOEFT, W. C. "The Negative Sequence Reactances of an Ideal Synchronous Machine." *Trans. A.I.E.E.*, 1949, vol. 68, page 510. | 192 |
| 50.1 | ROBERT, R. "Micro-machines and Micro-reseaux." *C.I.G.R.E.*, Paper No. 338, 1950. | 50 |
| 50.2 | KILGORE, L. A. and WHITNEY, E. C. "Spring and Damping Coefficients of Synchronous Machines and their Application." *Trans. A.I.E.E.*, 1950, vol. 69, page 226. | 172 |
| 51.1 | CONCORDIA, C. *Synchronous Machines* (book), John Wiley. | 3, 187 |
| 51.2 | LAIBLE, TH. *Die Theorie der Synchronmachine im Nicht-stationären Betrieb* (book), Springer, 1951. | 3, 5, 141, 173 |
| 51.3 | MACMILLAN, R. H. *Theory of Control* (book), Cambridge Univ. Press, 1951. | 83 |
| 51.4 | ALGER, P. L. *The Nature of Polyphase Induction Machines* (book), John Wiley, 1951. | 5 |
| 51.5 | ADKINS, B. and GIBBS, W. J. *Polyphase Commutator Machines* (book), Cambridge Univ. Press, 1951. | 223 |
| 51.6 | GIBBS, W. J. "The Modern Approach to Electrical Machine Analysis." *The Engineer*, 1951, Oct. 12th, *et seq.* Reprinted as B. T-H. *Technical Monograph* T.M.S. 757, with the title "Algebra of Electric Machine Analysis." | 4, 229 |
| 51.7 | ADKINS, B. "Transient Theory of Synchronous Generators Connected to Power Systems." *Jour. I.E.E.*, 1951, vol. 98, page 510. | 145, 154, 176 |
| 52.1 | GIBBS, W. J. *Tensors in Electrical Machine Theory* (book), Chapman and Hall, 1952. | 4 |
| 52.2 | MORTLOCK, J. R. and HUMPHREY DAVIES, M. W. *Power System Analysis* (book), Chapman and Hall, 1952. | 193 |
| 52.3 | TUSTIN, A. *Direct Current Machines for Control Systems* (book), E. & F. N. Spon, 1952. | 74 |
| 53.1 | BOWDEN, B. V. (Editor). *Faster than Thought* (book), Pitman, 1953. | 52 |

# CHRONOLOGICAL BIBLIOGRAPHY

| *Ref. No.* | *Book or Paper* | *Page* |
|---|---|---|
| 53.2 | HUMPHREY DAVIES, M. W. and SLEMON, G. R. "The Transformer Analogue Network Analyser." *Jour. I.E.E.*, 1953, vol. 99, Pt. II, page 469. | 51 |
| 54.1 | SAY, M. G. (Editor). *Rotating Amplifiers* (book), George Newnes, 1954. | 78 |
| 54.2 | CHING, Y. K. and ADKINS, B. "Transient Theory of Synchronous Generators under Unbalanced Conditions." *Jour. I.E.E.*, 1954, vol. 101, Pt. IV, page 166. | 188 |
| 54.3 | CHORLTON, A., ROBERT, R. and CONCORDIA, C. "Computational aids to Power System Analysis." *C.I.G.R.E.*, Paper No. 323, 1954. | 52 |

# INDEX

A.C. COMMUTATOR MACHINE, 38, 214, 216
Air-gap, 8
— M.M.F., 20, 87
— flux density, 9, 87
Amplidyne, 78, 83, 224
Amplifiers, 74
Analyser, 4, 48
— differential, 36, 51, 161
— network, 36, 48, 50, 114, 140, 193
— transformer analogue, 51
— transient, 51
Angular deviation, 164
Approximations, 4, 12, 26, 61, 69, 121,
  130, 147, 169, 174
Argand diagram, 39
Asynchronous machine, 38
Axis coils, 37, 101, 108, 201
— components of current, 96, 134
— — — flux linkage, 106
— — — M.M.F., 21, 95, 102

BLONDEL, 3
Brush, neutral position, 58, 63
— gear, 10, 13
— separation, 218
— shift, 63, 68, 212, 218
Build-up curve, 75

CARBON-PILE REGULATOR, 84
Circuit theory, 2, 5, 17
Closed-loop system, 83
Coil axis, 21
Coil, definition, 12
Commutator winding, 10, 14
Complex conjugate, 43
— numbers, 2, 4, 36, 39, 87
Computer, 4, 36, 48, 193
—, analogue, 48, 49
—, digital, 49, 51
Concentrated coils, 16
Concordia, 3, 187
Connection matrix, 207, 213, 222, 225,
  228
Constants of the machine, 1, 10, 22
Control systems, 5, 53, 74
Conventions, 4, 12, 13, 16, 30, 32, 55,
  169
Current distribution, 20
— matrix, 28

DESIGN METHODS, 1, 22, 23
Developed diagram, 8, 20

Diesel-driven generator, 66, 163, 171
Direct axis, 2, 12
Direct-current machine, 10, 13, 37, 53,
  74, 201, 212
Armature leakage, 57
— reaction, 22, 53, 63, 67, 78
Commutation, 53, 63
Compensating winding, 61, 79
Cross-field machine, 13, 78, 212
D.C. voltage ratio, 75
Field-form curve, 57
Generator and exciter, 74
Interpole winding, 61, 68
Motor, 80
Residual magnetism, 71
Self-excited machine, 53, 71
Separately excited machine, 58,
  67
Series winding, 61, 68
Short circuit, 64, 67
Speed-torque characteristic, 82
Time constant, armature, 68, 82
— —, field, 68, 75
— —, mechanical, 82
Transient resistance, 70
Doherty, 182
Doherty and Nickle, 3, 183, 187
Duesterhoeft, 192

EDDY CURRENTS, 68, 111, 167
Effective number of turns, 25, 118
Envelope curves, 151
Empirical methods, 22
Equations of the machine, 2, 23, 27
Equivalent circuit, 2
— two-phase winding, 126, 188, 201

FAULT CONDITIONS, 175, 191, 194
Feed-back, 83, 224
Flux, air-gap, 7, 20
—, axis of, 20
—, leakage, 16, 24, 57, 106, 220
—, main, 16, 25, 54, 220
Flux density wave, 9, 21
— linkage, 54, 105
Forced oscillations, 163
Free oscillations, 163

GENERAL EQUATIONS, 22, 29, 35, 101,
  129, 159, 201
— theory, 3, 15, 17, 27, 37, 55, 101,
  201

Generalised machine, 1, 3, 13, 29, 58, 108, 201
Gibbs, 4

HARMONIC WINDING FACTOR, 105, 108
— vector, 39
Harmonics, 23, 24, 58, 105, 142, 187
Heaviside, 5, 17, 36, 44, 68
Hunting, 164, 172

IDEALISED MACHINE, 2, 7, 11
Impedance matrix, 28, 205
Impressed voltage, 17, 18, 106
Induced voltage, 18
Inductance, complete, 18, 57, 112, 116
—, leakage, 18, 24, 106, 116, 220
—, magnetising, 116, 220
—, mutual, 18, 57, 101, 106, 112, 116, 220
—, zero-sequence, 107
Induction motor, 10, 24, 38, 88, 124, 201, 216, 226
    Equivalent circuit, 91, 140
    Injected voltage, 124, 218
    Leakage reactance, 94
    Magnetising current, 90
    — reactance, 91
Inductive circuit, 17, 41
Inertia, moment of, 31
'Infinite bus', 157
Initial value, 68, 78, 151, 179, 194
Interconnected systems, 83, 223
Internal voltage, 89, 106
Invariance of power, 206

KRON, 3, 4, 17, 37, 124

LAIBLE, 3
Laplace transform method, 5, 188
Leakage, 8, 16, 24, 57
Load study, 193

MAGNETOMOTIVE FORCE, 20, 87
M.M.F., axis of, 21
M.M.F. vector, 87, 89, 93
— wave, 21, 87
Matrices, 3, 28, 201
Matrix algebra, 28, 203
— equation, 28, 203
— multiplication, 203
— transformation, 201
Metadyne, 78
Method of equating coefficients, 107, 133, 136, 145, 160
Micro-machine and micro-system, 50

NATURAL FREQUENCY, 166

Non-linear effects, 22, 53, 84
— equations, 5, 36, 159
Notation, 4, 16, 19, 40, 68, 95, 124, 168, 203

OPERATIONAL IMPEDANCE, 113, 119
— methods, 36, 44, 68, 145
Original value, 65, 68
Oscillogram, analysis of, 73, 151

PARASITIC EFFECTS, 24
Park, 3, 17, 22, 31, 37, 101, 105, 124
Partial fractions, 46, 70, 147, 151, 161
Per-unit system, 6, 17, 57, 105, 116
— —, advantages, 19, 33
— —, axis currents, 102
— —, induction motor, 90
— —, mechanical units, 32, 165
— —, transformer, 17
'Phasor', 5
Power amplification, 75, 78
— angle characteristic, 97
— equation, 32, 34, 104, 109
— in A.C. circuits, 43, 210
— selsyns, 226
— system analysis, 174, 192
Primitive machine, 203
— network, 209
Pseudo-stationary coil, 15, 29, 38, 58, 78, 108

QUADRATURE AXIS, 2, 12

RANK OF MATRIX, 203
Reference axis, 97, 159
— voltage, 83, 224
Reluctance torque, 135
Repulsion motor, 214
Response curve, 78
Rotating flux wave, 86, 149
Rotation voltage, 30, 56, 109

SALIENT POLES, 8, 11, 21, 38, 88, 95, 105
Saturation, 22, 43, 53, 63, 77, 167, 200
Schrage motor, 216
Self-excitation, 163, 167, 172
Sinusoidal quantities, 39, 86
Sinusoidally distributed winding, 105
Small changes, 37, 64, 85
— oscillations, 37, 64, 85, 163, 168
Space harmonics, 23
— vector, 40, 86, 90, 93
Speed, nominal, 33
Squirrel cage, 10, 12, 112, 128
Stabilising transformer, 224
Stability, 64, 66, 84
—, steady-state, 193

Stability, transient, 175, 194
Starting of motors, 134
Steady operation, 27, 35, 60, 86, 132, 168, 175, 193, 215
Step-by-step method, 36, 77, 195
Step-function voltage, 45, 76
Stored energy, 33, 34
Superposition, principle of, 22, 30, 42, 45, 67, 95, 136, 146, 157, 199
Swing curve, 175, 195
Symmetrical components, 103, 128, 141, 187, 190
Synchronous machine, 10, 11, 38, 91, 110, 132, 201, 212
    Axis current and voltage, 101
    Constant-flux-linkage theorem, 182, 195
    Constants, list of, 122
    Cylindrical-rotor machine, 91, 175, 216
    Damper winding, 12, 111, 167
    Damping constant, 164, 168
    — torque, 164
    Elastic constant, 164, 168
    — torque, 164
    Equations, summary of, 121
    Equivalent circuit, 94, 114, 118, 139, 176, 179
    — mechanical system, 164
    Inertia constant, 33, 165
    Load angle, 97, 159, 175
    Negative damping, 167
    Reactance, effective synchronous, 194
    —, equivalent, 194
    —, leakage, 94, 122
    —, magnetising, 93, 95, 122
    —, negative sequence, 141, 190
    —, subtransient, 115, 123, 147, 154, 181, 192
    —, synchronous, 94, 96, 123, 133, 154, 181
    —, transient, 115, 123, 148, 175, 181
    —, zero-sequence, 191
    —, Potier, 22
    Saliency, transient and subtransient, 185
    Salient-pole machine, 95, 175
    Sudden application of load, 196
    — change of voltage, 156, 182
    — removal of load, 199

Synchronising, 135, 160
— torque coefficient, 99, 166
Time constant, armature, 149, 152, 154
— —, damper leakage, 122
— —, subtransient, 120, 122, 154
— —, transient, 120, 122, 154
Voltage behind synchronous, transient and subtransient reactance, 184, 193

TENSORS, 3
Terminology, 4, 106, 122
Time constant, 46, 76
— vector, 40, 86, 90, 93
Torque, applied, 31
—, electrical, 31, 34, 60
Torque equation, 2, 15, 31, 35, 60, 109
— pulsations, 66, 163
Transformer, 15, 45
— voltage, 30, 54, 109
Transformation, 3, 14, 31, 37, 97, 101, 126, 201
Transient operation, 27, 35
Transpose of matrix, 207
Two-axis theory, 2, 15, 38, 88, 95, 101, 108, 183

UNBALANCED OPERATION, 38, 144, 186
Unit step-function, 45

VECTOR, 2, 5, 39
— diagram, 2, 39, 86, 94, 96, 132, 176
— equation, 39, 42, 66, 90, 94, 96, 133, 137
Voltage equations, 2, 15, 28, 35, 54, 101
— matrix, 28
— regulator, 84, 175, 193, 199, 224

WARD-LEONARD SYSTEM, 81, 84
West, 3
Winding, classification, 10
—, definition, 12
—, fractional-slot, 9
Winding distribution, 20, 25, 105, 117
— factor, 25, 105

ZERO-SEQUENCE CURRENT, 101, 103, 109
— inductance, 107
— reactance, 191
— voltage, 101